Feedback
Loop Stability
Analysis

Circuit Solutions Series

BENSON • *Television Engineering Handbook, 2/e*

BEST • *Phase-Locked Loops, 3/e*

CHEN • *Fuzzy Logic and Neural Network Handbook*

COOMBS • *Printed Circuits Handbook, 4/e*

CHRISTIANSEN • *Electronics Engineers' Handbook, 4/e*

GRAEME • *Optimizing Op Amp Performance*

GRAEME • *Photodiode Amplifiers Op Amp Solutions*

HARPER • *Electronic Packaging and Interconnection Handbook, 2/e*

HARPER • *Passive Electronics Component Handbook*

HECHT • *Tee Laser Guidebook*

JURAN AND GRYNA • *Juran's Quality Control Handbook*

JURGEN • *Digital Consumer Electronics Handbook*

KIELKOWSKI • *Inside SPICE*

OSA • *Handbook of Optics, 2/e*

RORABAUGH • *Digital Filter Designer's Handbook, 2/e*

SERGENT AND HARPER • *Hybrid Microelectronic Handbook*

SMITH • *Thin-Film Deposition*

SZE • *VLSI Technology*

WAYNANT • *Electro-Optics Handbook*

WILLIAMS AND TAYLOR • *Electronic Filter Design Handbook*

ZOMAYA • *Parallel and Distributed Computing Handbook*

To order or receive additional information on these or any other McGraw-Hill titles, in the United States call 1-800-722-4726 or visit us at www.ee.mcgraw-hill.com. In other countries, contact your local McGraw-Hill representative.

Feedback Loop Stability Analysis

Walter S. Friauf

McGraw-Hill

New York   San Francisco   Washington, D.C.   Auckland   Bogotá
Caracas   Lisbon   London   Madrid   Mexico City   Milan
Montreal   New Delhi   San Juan   Singapore
Sydney   Tokyo   Toronto

Library of Congress Cataloging-in-Publication Data

Friauf, Walter S.
    Feedback loop stability analysis / Walter S. Friauf.
         p.   cm. — (Circuit solutions series)
    Includes index.
    ISBN 0-07-022844-2
    1. Electronic circuit design.   2. Feedback (Electronics)
    3. Feedback control systems.   I. Title.   II. Series.
    TK7867.F76   1998
    621.3815'35—dc21   97-48868
                                           CIP

McGraw-Hill

A Division of The McGraw-Hill Companies

1 2 3 4 5 6 7 8 9 0   FGR/FGR   9 0 3 2 1 0 9 8

ISBN 0-07-022844-2

The sponsoring editor for this book was Steve Chapman, the editing supervisor was Ruth W. Mannino, and the production supervisor was Tina Cameron. It was set in Palatino by Don Feldman of McGraw-Hill's desktop publishing department.

Printed and bound by Quebecor/Fairfield.

McGraw-Hill books are available at special quantity discounts to use as premiums and sales promotions, or for use in corporate training programs. For more information, please write to the Director of Special Sales, McGraw-Hill, 11 West 19th Street, New York, NY 10011. Or contact your local bookstore.

This book is printed on recycled, acid-free paper containing a minimum of 50% recycled, de-inked fiber.

Contents

Preface

With books on feedback control theory lining technical library shelves as far as the eye can see, there should be a specific rationale for every new volume. The objectives of this work include emphasis on minimum phase characteristics in order to optimize performance and to simplify analysis and design, much as linearity has been emphasized for the same purposes in most previous texts. New design curves for second- and third-order minimum phase systems have been developed to give closed-loop stability characteristics, both time and frequency domain, as a function of open-loop frequency domain parameters, in a very simple and easy fashion. Finally, the methods are extended to accommodate transport lags and systems of any higher order.

Many of the concepts involved were developed by H. W. Bode more than half a century ago but in the context of a very general mesh of bilateral elements that required a difficult mathematical treatment. Now that most feedback systems include an operational amplifier, a much simpler unilateral loop approach is usually sufficient. When this simplification is combined with that conferred by minimum phase and the new design curves, the surprising simplicity of this text results. The modest level of mathematics needed should make the book appropriate for courses at junior colleges and technical schools, as well as for conventional feedback courses and for working engineers. It could also be of interest to physicians, medical researchers, and others who have no plans to design feedback control systems, but who encounter them in their work and would like to know more about their virtues

and stability problems. It is largely for the benefit of this audience that
the book starts out very slowly, so trained engineers will probably scan
or skip the first few chapters. Almost all material on other methods
has been omitted, leading to a short and easy book but with space for
many useful sidelights and practical matters that are missing , for the
most part, from traditional feedback texts.

As to prerequisites, high school algebra is a necessity, and a first-
year college math course including complex numbers and calculus is
desirable, although very little calculus is actually used. A little ac circuit theory and familiarity with Fourier transforms would also be
highly desirable.

A valid question in the computer age is whether any method not
based on computer simulation or processing is worth studying. Some
of the more difficult traditional methods may well not be, but a very
simple and easy approach should still be worthwhile for several reasons. It allows the engineer to avoid total dependence on a computer, a
state some of us old-timers have never fully accepted. It facilitates an
understanding of how the mathematics relates to physical reality,
which is often obscured by more complex approaches and computer
simulations and is necessary for full utilization of the power of computers. Finally, it develops an appreciation of how to attack problems
confidently and successfully with simple tools and full heuristic
understanding of what is going on, something that should never
become obsolete for the true engineering spirit.

This book pursues an intermediate course in regard to this matter.
Computer simulations have been used extensively, but mainly to
develop simple design curves rather than to attack problems directly,
and also to reduce the amount and level of math needed. At the same
time one of the design curves is developed completely without help
from a computer, and a similar course for some of the others is out-
lined.

Acknowledgments are in order for former teachers and colleagues
too numerous to cite individually except for the following. Les Jasper
first directed my attention to the importance of minimum phase characteristics, as well as other important subjects including the double
helix and a transistor model based on Sah's equations, when we were
both engineers at Texas Instruments 37 years ago. More recently, several fellow engineers in the Biomedical Engineering and
Instrumentation Program at the National Institutes of Health (NIH)
were extremely helpful. Wardell J. Lindsay provided valuable intellec-
tual stimulation; Currie Wooten helped with computer simulations;
and Horace Cascio, Tom Clem, Joe Fessler, and Tom Pohida reviewed a
preliminary draft and provided valuable comments.

It is also appropriate to mention that some of the material was originally developed, although in less complete form, about 25 years ago for an evening course taught at NIH under the auspices of the Foundation for Advanced Education in the Sciences. All the computer simulations were performed with an evaluation program provided by MicroSim Corporation.

Walter S. Friauf

1
Introduction to Feedback

Basic Concepts

"I could drive that road blindfolded." This oft-heard saying does not mean what it says, nor is it intended to, but rather uses extreme exaggeration to emphasize how well someone knows a given road. Everyone realizes that driving blindfolded is impossible under any conditions because of unpredictable crosswinds, steering-gear wear, and the like, not to mention other drivers. The advantage of not being blindfolded is the ability to see where the car is in a lane, among other things, and for the sake of simplicity we will confine the following discussion to the control of lateral position. The visual sensing of position provides *feedback* to the driver, which is one of the four things needed for any feedback control system. Next is an *input* or *reference* that specifies the value that the controlled variable should have. For this example the input could include lane stripes, knowledge from driver education, and convention in the country where the driving took place. The next essential element is a *comparator* that compares the actual sensed position, or feedback signal, with the desired position, or reference signal. In our example comparison would occur in the brain of the driver, but when a person is not part of the loop, it is usually accomplished by subtracting the two signals via either hardware or software. The output of the comparator is usually called an *error signal* whose polarity determines which way a correction needs to be made.

The final essential is a *control mechanism*, which is activated by the error signal and results in a correction of the position. For our example the control mechanism is the neurological and muscular systems of the driver and the complete steering system of the car, which might include power steering to amplify the force. The feedback is negative in that it causes a correction to be made in the direction that is opposite to, or the negative of, the deviation from the desired position. Positive feedback also has its uses, as in bistable devices and oscillators, but this book considers only negative feedback.

Since the four elements just mentioned, reference input, comparator, control mechanism, and sensing of the controlled parameter, are essential features of a feedback control system, it follows that any scheme to control something that lacks one or more of these elements is not a feedback control system. Thus, it is easy to assess many legislative programs and obvious why so many of them fail. It also follows, looking at things in a general way, that nothing can be controlled by feedback unless it can be measured.

Benefits of Feedback

The desired lateral position is the only intentional input to the system just described, but several other factors such as crosswind, centrifugal force, misaligned steering gear, and slope of the road can also affect the position. Such inputs, being unwanted, are often called *disturbances* and, since they are subject to unknown change with time, are responsible for the impossibility of driving blindfolded. One of the main reasons for using feedback control is to virtually eliminate the effect of disturbances. However, this is by no means the only reason. In many control situations it is desirable to have the output exactly proportional to the input, but the amplifiers, motors, and other components used to develop the output will usually not be perfectly linear. We will see later that the use of two precision resistors and feedback can greatly reduce nonlinearities in all other system components except the sensor used to provide the feedback signal. In addition, when systems are being mass-produced with inexpensive components that may have a considerable variation in values, feedback can greatly reduce the effect of the variation from one unit to another.

Feedback also allows the apparent response speed of a component such as a motor to be increased by overdriving it when rapid response is desired. The improvement will be proportional to the amount of overdrive, which, in turn, is proportional to the loop gain. Still another reason to use feedback is to provide a stiff output, which means an output that is not susceptible to being changed by disturbances. The lateral position of an automobile is very easily influenced by cross-wind in the absence of feedback, in contrast to a railway car, for example, where flanged wheels provide extreme stiffness without feedback. With feedback, however, the automobile can exhibit behavior almost as stiff.

Problems of Feedback

If all these benefits sound almost too good to be true, it is time for a reality check. Actually, they are true enough, but it is also true that there are no free rides in this world. There are two main costs. First is an increase in system complexity, which may increase component count, although that may be offset by the possibility of using cheaper components. The second is more serious, and it introduces a stability problem. This problem is sufficiently troublesome that 90 percent of the pages of all books on feedback are devoted to it. By *stability problem* we mean a tendency to overcontrol, or overshoot, when the input or a disturbance changes suddenly. Alternatively, in the frequency domain, the gain may rise near the upper end of the passband, which is usually undesirable. Audio and video amplifiers, for example, should have virtually flat response throughout their passband. In an extreme case the gain can become high enough to cause oscillation, that is, a sustained cyclic output without any input. This effect renders the system useless and may destroy part of the control system or that which it is controlling.

Causes of Instability

The stability problem is inevitable and results from the fact that the feedback, which is connected so as to be negative at low frequencies, usually becomes positive at high frequencies. Good stability is still possible provided the loop gain is low enough, and the rest of this book is devoted to exploring the conditions necessary for maintaining stability. The main reason that the feedback ultimately becomes positive as the frequency increases is that both the control system and the load it is driving contain components that can store energy. *Capacitance* and *inductance* are electrical energy storage elements, and *mass* and *elastance* are mechanical energy storage elements. Since the drive to such elements is finite, the response must dwindle toward zero as the frequency approaches infinity, with a concomitant phase shift approaching 90°. Several phase shifts can add up so that the total around the loop equals 360°, which is positive feedback. Only 180° of additional shift from the energy storage elements is needed to cause positive feedback, since the connection at the comparator introduces 180° to make the feedback negative at low frequencies. Transport lags, if present, also contribute phase shift.

Historical Perspective

Historically, the stability problem was first clearly recognized when centrifugal fly-ball governors were applied to early steam engines shortly after their invention around the middle of the eighteenth century. It was approximately another century before the first mathematical analysis of this problem was carried out by the eminent scientist James Clerk Maxwell, who is far more famous for his celebrated electromagnetic theory of light. He formulated the problem in terms of differential equations and deduced from them the relations between parameter values and stability. This procedure was followed for the few analyses of feedback systems that were carried out until well into the twentieth century when Nyquist, Bode, and many others laid the foundations of modern control theory and developed methods of analysis that are easier to use than the direct application of differential equations. The demands of World War II and automation in the postwar years led to the development of a considerable variety of techniques, many of them oriented toward the more difficult and challenging problems of the times. We want to revisit this material, identify the simplest tools that are adequate for the bulk of the simpler problems, and apply them to the stabilization problem. In so doing, we will rely on computer simulations to a considerable degree to minimize the distraction of excessive mathematics.

2
Loop
Characteristics

Mesh and Loop Models for Feedback

The problem of steering a car is an example of a fairly simple feedback control system. A vastly more complicated example would be the national economy, with inputs such as the Federal Reserve rate, minimum wage, money supply, tariffs, and the like and with outputs such as the gross national product, the distribution thereof, unemployment, and many others. Almost everything mentioned has some effect on most of the others and is affected by most of the others to some degree, blurring the distinction between inputs and outputs. To depict the situation graphically requires a mesh diagram in which each node represents a parameter and interconnections between them represent cause-effect relationships. Many of the links will be bilateral; that is, each one of a pair of parameters will have a direct effect on the other, in addition to effects involving pathways through several other nodes. Even when the system is a much simpler electrical network, such an approach is quite complicated from both conceptual and mathematical standpoints. It has been carried out by Bode (1945), but fortunately will not be needed for the somewhat simpler objectives we are pursuing. For most feedback control systems, a *unilateral-loop* model is adequate and far simpler. By *unilateral* we mean that significant signal flow in the loop is in only one direction, normally clockwise as figures are usually drawn. Any signal flow in the opposite direction is so small that it can be totally ignored. The main reason that this much simpler model is usually adequate is that most feedback control systems now include an operational amplifier in the gain path, and its characteristics block any significant signal flow in a reverse direction.

Loop Equations

Figure 2-1 shows the model we will be using for most of the book. It includes the four components mentioned as essential in Chap. 1 plus a feedback network that is usually, but not always, present. Signal flow is from left to right, except through the feedback network B, where it must be from right to left because of clockwise flow around the loop. This convention is so well established that arrows to indicate direction are usually used only at the summing junction, or comparator, which is the circle with the X in it. The inputs—two in this case, but there can be any number—have arrowheads and + or − signs to indicate whether each input is to be added or subtracted. With two inputs and the polarities shown, the summing junction is simply subtracting two signals, which is in effect performing the comparison that is one of the functions needed for every feedback loop.

The input is labeled R for reference, the output is C for controlled variable, and the output of the summing junction is E for error signal. Writing equations, we find

$$C = AE$$

$$E = R - BC$$

Eliminating E, since it is an internal parameter, and solving for the overall gain of the system, we get Eq. (2.1).

$$\frac{C}{R} = \frac{A}{1 + AB}$$

$$= \frac{1}{B} \frac{1}{1 + 1/AB} \qquad (2.1)$$

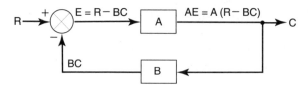

Figure 2.1. Basic unilateral feedback loop.

The second form, with $1/B$ factored out, looks more complicated but is actually more convenient for most purposes, since C/R will be almost exactly $1/B$ for all useful feedback loops. The reason is that AB will usually be much greater than one, making the other factor in the second form almost unity. If desired, the second factor can be written $(1 + 1/AB)^{-1}$ and expanded with the binomial theorem to give $(1 - 1/AB)$ when all the higher-order terms, which will usually be negligible, are discarded.

The overall gain, C/R, is called the *closed-loop gain,* since it is the gain from input to output with the loop closed and operating; it is the only gain of any final interest. Strictly speaking, it is not a loop gain at all, despite the name, but rather the system gain when the loop is closed. The real loop gain is the product of all the gains around the loop, AB, and is referred to as the *open-loop gain,* or frequently just the *loop gain.* This gain could be measured, theoretically, by opening the loop anywhere, inserting a test signal, measuring the signal that appears at the other end of the break, and calculating the ratio. It is actually a loop gain only when the loop is closed, but by convention it is called the *open-loop gain.*

We are ignoring until the next chapter the effect of energy storage elements in network A or B. The energy storage elements are inevitable, and give rise to the stability problem. In most instances the significant energy storage elements are confined to network A, which is usually more complex, since it must provide sufficient amplification to drive the output and to make AB much greater than unity. Network A will also need a source of power, which is not shown explicitly in Fig. 2-1, and it may not be entirely linear. Network B, in contrast, is usually passive, and every effort is made to make it highly linear. Being passive, the gain will be unity or less (excluding the unlikely possibility of a step-up transformer), and it will often be much less than one if a high value of closed-loop gain is desired, since B is almost exactly the reciprocal of the closed-loop gain.

Loop Examples

The simple but widely used circuit shown in Fig. 2-2 illustrates these points and conforms exactly to the block diagram of Fig. 2-1. Since this circuit is entirely electrical, appropriate alternate notation is used for the input voltage e_i and the output voltage e_o. The triangular symbol is an operational amplifier (op amp for short), which is discussed more fully in Chap. 13. For the present we need know only that the output is A times the difference between the voltages at the + and − inputs. The

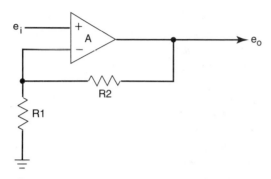

Figure 2.2. Feedback voltage amplifier.

op amp is clearly serving as both the summing junction, or comparator, and network A. The feedback network is a voltage divider with gain from right to left, as shown below.

$$B = R1/(R1 + R2)$$

For concreteness let us assume the following numerical values:

$$A = 1,000,000$$

$$R1 = 1\,k\Omega$$

$$R2 = 99\,k\Omega$$

Then $B = 1/100$, the loop gain is $AB = 10,000$, and the closed-loop gain is

$$e_o/e_i = 100(1-1/10,000)$$

$$= 99.99$$

which is very close to $1/B$ indeed, because AB is so much greater than unity. Assuming that the objective is a gain of precisely 100, the value of B must be controlled very accurately. We can achieve this control easily and inexpensively by using precision resistors for $R1$ and $R2$.

The value assumed for A might seem surprisingly high, but is not unusual for many modern op amps at low frequencies. It might well be given as a typical value on the specification sheet, with a minimum value of 500,000, and no limit on the maximum value. This wide range allows considerable latitude in production, resulting in a very low price. However, the closed-loop gain would vary only from 99.98 to

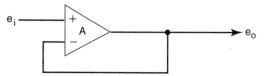

Figure 2.3. Feedback voltage follower.

100, as can be verified by substituting the other values of A in the equation for closed-loop gain. One price for this convenience is a closed-loop gain much less than the open-loop gain of the op amp, but a closed-loop gain of 1,000,000 can be obtained by simply cascading three of the circuits. This technique would provide a precise gain much more economically than could be obtained without feedback. Also, of course, the gain would be much more stable, since the effect of changes in amplifier gain with time, temperature, and other factors would be virtually eliminated.

To achieve a closed-loop gain of one B must be one, and a direct connection from the output to the inverting input of the op amp would suffice, as shown in Fig. 2-3. This configuration, commonly referred to as a *voltage follower*, since the output voltage tracks or follows the input voltage, is an example of a feedback loop without a feedback network, unless you want to view the direct connection as a network with unity gain. We should also note that because the input and output are both the same type of variable (that is, voltages) in these examples, the feedback network can be connected directly to the output without a separate transducer to sense the output variable. If the input and output were different types of variables, a transducer would be necessary, and its sensitivity or gain would have to be included in B.

Effect of Feedback on Nonlinearity in the Forward Path

So far we have assumed that A is linear, which means that it is a fixed number independent of signal level. If it is not, another benefit of feedback will appear. Suppose that the output current capability of the op amp in Fig. 2-3 is insufficient to drive the load so that a complementary emitter follower is added as shown in Fig. 2-4. The complementary emitter follower has a considerable nonlinearity near the origin, shown in Fig. 2-5, because of the base emitter voltage drops of the

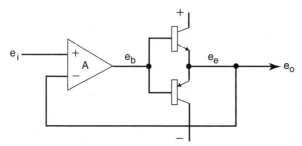

Figure 2.4. Feedback voltage follower with complementary emitter follower output stage.

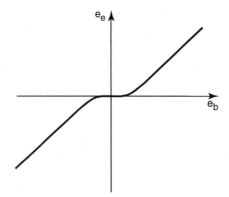

Figure 2.5. Static gain characteristic of complementary emitter follower.

transistors. If the drive to the complementary emitter follower were a sine wave, the output would be as shown in Fig. 2-6. However, with feedback the insufficient output voltage at low values would cause a smaller feedback signal, resulting in an increased value of e_b where needed to overcome the base emitter drops and give a highly linear overall response. This response is shown in Fig. 2-7 for a sine wave input of about 0.7 V rms and an amplifier gain of 30. This value is essentially the open-loop gain, since the gain of the feedback network is unity, as is the gain of the complementary emitter follower except for the decrease at low signal levels. With a larger signal the effect of the crossover distortion is less pronounced, and vice versa. This result is apparent in Fig. 2-8, which shows the base drive and output for the same circuit when the input is only one-tenth as large.

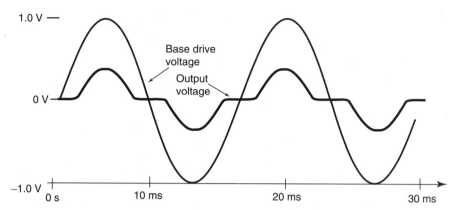

Figure 2.6. Complementary emitter follower output voltage with sine wave input.

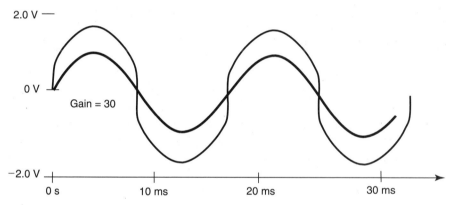

Figure 2.7. Base drive and output of emitter follower output stage in feedback loop with sine wave input.

Figures 2-7 and 2-8 illustrate the marked improvement provided by feedback, compared to the output in Fig. 2-6, even with a rather modest open-loop gain. Some requirements, however, such as a high-fidelity amplifier, need much higher gain. The ear is very sensitive to crossover distortion, which does an excellent job of mimicking speaker rattle. Experimental work at the lowest level that needed to be handled would be necessary to determine the minimum value of gain needed, because of the subjective nature of what is satisfactory.

The base drive voltage needed to give an output proportional to the input depends on the input waveform, signal level, transistor charac-

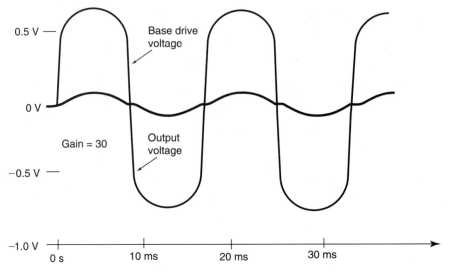

Figure 2.8. Same curves as in Fig. 2.7 except at much lower signal level.

teristics, and the load. The modification in base drive waveform required when a capacitor is added in parallel with a resistive load appears in Fig. 2-9, still with a sinusoidal input. A high-gain feedback loop automatically adjusts the base drive to the complementary emitter follower to accommodate any changes in the parameters just mentioned. Incidentally, the curves in Figs. 2-6 through 2-9 were developed with computer simulations of the circuit shown in Fig. 2-4. (Coverage of this topic continues with Chap. 10.)

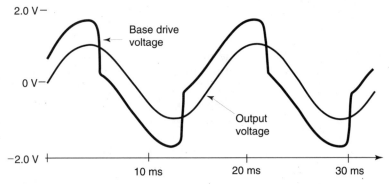

Figure 2.9. Same curves as in Fig. 2.7 except with capacitor added in parallel with load resistor.

Effect of Feedback on
Stiffness of Output

Returning to the circuit of Fig. 2-2, we will now look at the effect of feedback on the stiffness of the output, or, in this case, the output impedance. The lower the output impedance, the stiffer the output. Suppose that the output impedance of the A path is 10 Ω in the absence of feedback, and that the input voltage is zero. The output voltage will then be zero also if no disturbance is applied to the output. However, let us assume that a disturbing current of 1 Å is injected into the output. The injection of this current will develop a voltage of 10 V at the output, according to Ohm's law. If the feedback is then connected, one-hundredth of that voltage, or 0.1 V will be fed back to the $-$ input of the op amp, using the same loop parameters assumed at the beginning of the chapter. That would be multiplied by the gain of the op amp, 1,000,000, resulting in an output of 100,000 V to oppose the 10 V developed by the disturbance. Actually, of course, only enough voltage would result to almost cancel the voltage due to the disturbance, since the near cancellation reduces the voltage fed back. To be precise, the bucking voltage from the A path needs to be 10 V, calling for an error signal of 10 microvolts (μV), which would result from 1 millivolt (mV) at the output. Thus the feedback reduces the voltage caused by a 1 Å disturbance by a factor of 10,000, which is just the loop gain AB.

Throughout this discussion we have ignored the possibility of significant signal flow around the loop in a counterclockwise direction. This treatment is reasonable because modern op amps have virtually no signal transfer from output to input and thus block counterclockwise flow in the loop. Individual transistors have enough reverse gain, mainly via collector-to-base capacitance, that it is frequently specified on data sheets as h_{12}, even though much smaller than the forward gain. For op amps, however, the reverse gain is so small that it is never even mentioned on data sheets and can safely be ignored. Linearity is another characteristic that is seldom mentioned on op amp data sheets, since enough feedback will almost always be used to greatly reduce the op amp's deficiencies.

Despite the extreme simplicity of Eq. (2.1), it gives a complete description of unilateral feedback loops when A and B correctly characterize all their respective components. We now need to diverge for a little while to look at the characterization of A and B, after which we will be in a position to explore the full consequences of Eq. (2.1).

3
Transfer Functions

Definition of Transfer Function

The characteristics of loop components can be described either by mathematical expressions, called *transfer functions*, or by graphs, which we will take up in the next chapter. Transfer function is a fancy name for gain, albeit a somewhat complicated gain in many cases. The expressions *open-loop gain* and *open-loop transfer function* are often used interchangeably in feedback literature, as are *closed-loop gain* and *closed-loop transfer function*. In the simplest situation the gain of a network or component is just a number that the input is multiplied by to give the output. If several components are connected in series, the individual gains are multiplied together to give the overall gain. A simple example is the voltage divider that constituted network B in Chap. 2. For that network, the transfer function, usually denoted by the letter w, is $R1/(R1 + R2)$. If $R1 = R2$, $w = 0.5$ and if two such networks were cascaded, with buffering to prevent loading effects, the overall gain would be the product 0.25. Since a voltage divider attenuates a signal, instead of amplifying it, the gain is less than unity, which means that if it is given in decibels, it is negative.

For a voltage divider, multiplying the input by the gain will give the output, regardless of the nature of the input, such as a dc value, sine wave, square wave, a transient, or whatever. At every instant the output is simply a fixed fraction of the input. The reason for this simplicity in the case of a voltage divider is that no energy can be stored, so the output at any instant depends only on the input at that instant and not on previous values. Many networks or components, however, have one or more elements capable of energy storage, which complicates matters. Examples of such elements are capacitance, inductance, mass, and elastance.

Calculating Frequency Domain Transfer Functions

When energy storage elements are present, the output at any instant depends on the current value of the input, and also to some degree on previous values. Furthermore, the way previous values affect the output depends on the waveform of the input. We will address this situation by looking at the simple network with energy storage capability shown in Fig. 3-1. This network is one of the most important networks encountered in feedback loops and is commonly referred to as a *lag network,* or just as a *lag.* The capacitor, C, by definition, stores a charge q when there is a voltage e across it according to relation (3.1)

$$q = Ce \tag{3.1}$$

and the stored energy is $(1/2)Ce^2$. Differentiating Eq. (3.1) gives Eq. (3.2)

$$i = \frac{dq}{dt} = C \frac{de}{dt} \tag{3.2}$$

which shows that the current is proportional to the rate of change of the voltage across the capacitor, rather than to the voltage itself as is the case with a resistor.

Since transfer functions are always calculated with the output open, or unloaded, the current in the capacitor will be the same as the current in the resistor. Therefore we have Eq. (3.3)

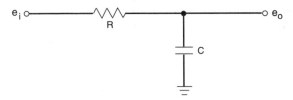

Figure 3.1. *RC* section, or lag network.

$$\frac{(e_i - e_o)}{R} = C\,\frac{de_o}{dt} \tag{3.3}$$

as a differential equation giving a complete relationship between e_i and e_o, regardless of the nature of e_i, but not in a very convenient form. There are several ways to get to a simpler relation, and the one we will pursue is to restrict the input voltage to be a sine wave, $e_i = \sin(\omega t)$, where the Greek letter ω stands for angular frequency, $2\pi f$, and f is the frequency in hertz, or as it used to be called, cycles per second. Thus the angle increases by 2π rad, or $360°$, for every increase in time of one period, or $1/f$ s.

Looking at the capacitor by itself for a moment, we find that with a sinusoidal voltage, Eq. (3.2) becomes Eq. (3.4):

$$\begin{aligned} i &= (C\omega)\cos \omega t \\ &= (C\omega)\sin(\omega t + \pi/2) \\ &= (C\omega)\,j\,\sin \omega t \\ &= (C\omega)\,j\,e \end{aligned} \tag{3.4}$$

where t = time

The imaginary number $j = \sqrt{-1}$ has been introduced to indicate the $90°$ phase shift between the voltage and the current. The current is a sine wave of the same frequency as the voltage and leads it in phase by $90°$. If we solve for e instead of for i, we find

$$\begin{aligned} e &= i(1/j\omega C) \\ &= iX \end{aligned} \tag{3.5}$$

where $X = 1/j\omega C$

X is called the reactance of the capacitor. Equation (3.5) is exactly like Ohm's law except with reactance playing the role that resistance normally plays. This equation can be used for all circuit calculations, the only difference being that, since X is an imaginary number, complex numbers result when resistors are also involved. You can find a more thorough discussion of this topic in any text on basic ac circuit analysis.

We can now return to the lag network and write its transfer function, using Ohm's law and Kirchhoff's laws, the same as for a resistive voltage divider.

$$\begin{aligned} w &= X/(R + X) \\ &= 1/(1 + R/X) \\ &= 1/(1 + j\omega RC) \\ &= 1/(1 + j\omega T) \end{aligned} \tag{3.6}$$

The product RC is usually called the *time constant* of the circuit and is indicated by T, as in the final form of Eq. (3.6). To emphasize that this form of transfer function is valid only for sinusoidal inputs, it is frequently written as

$$w(j\omega) = 1/(1 + j\omega T)$$

and is called the *frequency domain transfer function.*

Since it is a complex number with real and imaginary components, the frequency domain transfer function conveys two elements of information. The significance of these elements is clearer if we convert the function to polar form. Figure 3-2 shows the geometrical relations. The amplitude of the denominator is the square root of the sum of the squares of 1 and ωT, and the angle is the inverse tangent of ωT. When we take the reciprocal of the denominator to find w, the magnitude is inverted and the sign of the angle is reversed, leading to Eq. (3.7).

$$w(j\omega) = \left[1/\sqrt{(1 + \omega^2 T^2)} \right] \angle -\tan^{-1} \omega T \qquad (3.7)$$

The magnitude of w is a real number just like the ratio of a voltage divider, although it is a function of frequency instead of being constant, and the amplitude of the input sine wave is multiplied by the

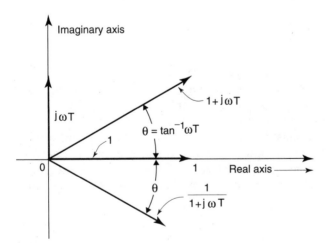

Figure 3.2. Phase and amplitude relations for a lag network.

magnitude of w to get the amplitude of the output. Then, in addition, the phase of the output is shifted relative to the input by another function of frequency, the inverse tangent of ωT.

Transfer Functions for Cascaded Networks

If two networks or components are cascaded, the output of the first will be the input to the second, so the overall output will be

$$e_o = [(e_i)w_1]w_2$$

$$= e_i(w_1 w_2)$$

Thus, we can combine the effects of two cascaded networks by multiplying their magnitudes and adding their phase shifts. This approach assumes that the loading effect of the second network on the first is negligible, which is the case if the impedance level of the second network is much higher than that of the first or if a buffer amplifier is used between them. If neither of these conditions exists, the effect of the loading can be taken into account by modifying the transfer function of the first network appropriately, or, which is essentially equivalent, by developing a transfer function for the two networks together from scratch.

Application of Frequency Domain Transfer Function to Time Domain Signals

Thus, we have arrived at a transfer function that is quite simple and satisfactory, except for the slight additional complications of the phase shift and dependency on frequency, plus the restriction to sine wave inputs. The latter might seem like an excessively high price to pay, but it is not really too bad thanks to Fourier's theorem. It states that any input can be resolved into sine wave components, each of which can then be processed individually by the frequency domain transfer function, the results added, and, inverse Fourier transformed back to give the output waveform. Fortunately, we will not actually have to carry out this tedious process. We will soon see that the fact that it is theoretically possible is all we really need. The process appears in block diagram form in Fig. 3-3. Any text on Fourier series and integrals, such as (Weaver, 1983), will provide more information on this topic.

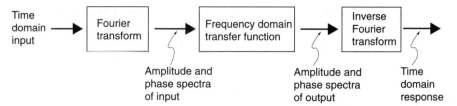

Figure 3.3. Scheme for processing time domain signals with a frequency domain transfer function.

Review of the Transfer Function of a Lag Network

Now let us examine the transfer function for the lag network in more detail. Either Eq. (3.6) or Eq. (3.7) shows that at very low frequencies, where ωT will be much smaller than one, the transfer function is almost exactly one and the phase shift is very small. When the frequency has increased enough that $\omega T = 1$, the denominator will be the square root of two, or 1.414, at an angle of 45°. When inverted, the transfer function becomes 0.707 at an angle of −45°. This frequency is commonly called the *cutoff frequency, break frequency,* or *corner frequency.* At very high frequencies, where ωT is much larger than one, the gain decreases inversely with frequency, and the phase increases to a constant value of −90°. The negative phase, or phase lag, at high frequencies accounts for the name of the circuit.

At frequencies far below the cutoff frequency, where ωT is much less than one, the phase angle is almost $-\omega T$, since the inverse tangent function and the angle, in radians, are almost equal for low values. Thus the phase well below cutoff, though small, is directly proportional to T, and varies linearly with frequency. Also, under these conditions, the magnitude component of Eq. (3.7) can be expanded with the aid of the binomial theorem. All terms beyond the first two will be negligible, giving Eq. (3.8):

$$w = 1 - (1/2)(\omega T)^2 \tag{3.8}$$

Since ωT, a small quantity, appears squared here, but only to the first power in the phase calculation, significant phase shift will occur long before any appreciable attenuation occurs as the frequency is increased toward the cutoff frequency. Anyone who has looked at a Lissajous figure for this type of circuit in electronics lab will recall that as the frequency is increased, the low-frequency pattern, a straight line at about 45°, opens up into an ellipse as the result of phase shift long before the

y-axis deflection decreases noticeably. We will see in Chap. 9 how this phenomenon can have an adverse effect on loop stability.

We will also need transfer functions for several other elements, but instead of developing them now, we will wait until after a means for depicting their characteristics graphically is developed in Chap. 4. Then we will be able to develop both characterizations for each network concurrently, which gives additional insight into their features.

4
Bode Plots

Since a graphical approach is usually the easiest way to analyze and design feedback loops, it is advantageous to be able to depict the information contained in transfer functions graphically. There are several ways to do so, but the method suggested by H. W. Bode in the 1930s (Bode, 1945) and ultimately named after him, is particularly useful. This method consists of plotting two curves, the log of gain, and phase, as functions of the log of frequency. Usually the gain in decibels, abbreviated dB, and the phase are plotted linearly along the y axis on graph paper that has several cycles of a log scale on the x axis. Each cycle represents a factor of ten in frequency. This special paper is known as *semilog graph paper* and is essential for making Bode plots.

Definition of Decibel

The decibel is a logarithmic measure of a ratio, which in this discussion is always a voltage ratio, or gain. It is defined, for this role, by Eq. (4.1)

$$dB = 20 \log(e_o/e_i) \qquad (4.1)$$

or by the equivalent exponential form in Eq. (4.2).

$$e_o/e_i = 10^{dB/20} \qquad (4.2)$$

The calculation can easily be done mentally with the aid of a small table of values (Table 4-1), which you should memorize. The memorization is made easier because reciprocal values of gain convert to the same value of decibel, except for sign.

Table 4-1. Table of
Decibel Values

Voltage ratio or gain	dB
1/100	−40
1/10	−20
1/2	−6
$1/\sqrt{2}$	−3
1	0
$\sqrt{2}$	3
2	6
3.16	10
5	14
10	20
100	40

Because of the properties of logarithms, when networks are cascaded so that their gains multiply, the overall gain in decibels is obtained by adding the decibels of the networks. Thus three cascaded networks with gains of 2, 2, and 10 would have a composite gain of $2 \times 2 \times 10 = 40$, for example, and the gains in decibels would combine as $6 + 6 + 20 = 32$ dB. The same idea makes it easy to convert to and from decibels by breaking down a total into its components. The numbers just used make it easy to convert a gain of 40 to 32 dB mentally. An example going the other way is 34 dB, which is $14 + 14 + 6$ dB, so the gain is $5 \times 5 \times 2 = 50$.

Bode Plots for a Lag Network

We are now ready to make a Bode plot and will start with the lag network discussed analytically in the preceding chapter. The sole parameter characterizing such a network is its time constant T, and we will arbitrarily take this to be 1 ms for this exercise. The break frequency is then $f = 1/(2\pi T) = 160$ Hz, approximately. At low frequencies the gain is flat and unity, or 0 dB. At high frequencies the gain rolls off inversely with frequency, decreasing by a factor of 2, or 6 dB, for every doubling of the frequency, which is an increase of one octave wherever it occurs. Alternatively, the roll-off rate can be expressed as 20 dB per decade (a factor of 10 in frequency), which results in a straight line on semilog graph paper with a slope of −6 dB/octave, intersecting the low-frequency curve at the break frequency. See Fig. 4-1, where we are using

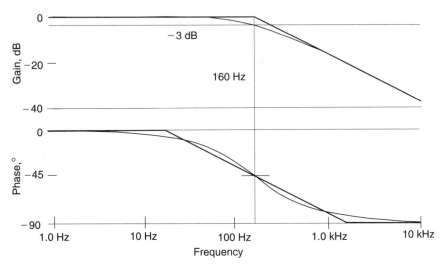

Figure 4-1. Bode gain and phase plots for a lag network.

four-cycle semilog graph paper with the x-axis scale selected to put the break frequency near the middle, and the y-axis scale selected to give a moderate slope. The two straight line segments constitute an asymptotic representation of the lag characteristic, which is not quite exact near the break frequency. There the gain is actually $1/\sqrt{(1 + 1)} = 0.707$, or -3 dB. Calculating more points enables us to draw the curve as accurately as desired, but the single 3 dB down point and the two asymptotes suffice to eyeball it. Even that is seldom done, however, since the process entails extra effort. In addition, the asymptotic form is generally more useful, since it shows the break frequency explicitly, which is desirable.

Although the x axis in Fig. 4-1 is a log frequency scale, the values of frequency are indicated directly for convenience. Consequently, as far as the numbers are concerned, it is a frequency scale, but the frequency markings are not spaced uniformly.

Turning now to the phase plot, we recall from Chap. 3 that it is 0 well below cutoff, $-90°$ well above, and $-45°$ at the break frequency. We also recall that the transition is more gradual than that of the gain characteristic, so that a few more points have been calculated, as shown in Table 4-2.

The simplest possible asymptotic phase plot jumps 90° at the break frequency. This plot has the virtue of extreme simplicity, and the value relates directly to the slope of the asymptotic gain plot in a way we will look at more closely in Chap. 5. However, because of the rather

Table 4-2. Gain and Phase Shift of Lag Network

ω	f	ωT	$\theta,°$	Amplitude	Amplitude, dB
0	0	0	0	1	0
$1/(4T)$	$1/(8\pi T)$	1/4	-14	0.97	-0.26
$1/(2T)$	$1/(4\pi T)$	1/2	-26.6	0.89	-1
$1/T$	$1/(2\pi T)$	1	-45	0.71	-3
$2/T$	$1/(\pi T)$	2	-63.4	0.55	-5.2
$4/T$	$2/(\pi T)$	4	-76	0.24	-12.4

slow transition of the phase, it is not very accurate. A much better approximation results from drawing a straight line through the points: 0° at a frequency one-tenth of the break frequency and −90° at 10 times the break frequency. On a Bode plot the line will be exact at the break frequency, showing a phase of −45°, with a maximum error at any frequency of about 6°. This type of approximation is seldom rounded to an accurate shape for the same reasons that apply to the gain curve, plus another one. For the lag network and for many others that constitute a subset known as *minimum phase networks* (MPNs), the phase characteristic contains no information in addition to that carried by the gain characteristic; therefore, the phase characteristic is often not plotted at all. These networks are so important that we will return to a more thorough discussion of them in the next chapter. Bode gain and phase plots for a lag network appear in Fig. 4-1. Although a time constant of 1 ms was used for Fig. 4-1, the value was completely arbitrary. The curves look exactly the same for any time constant except that the lateral position along the frequency scale changes.

It is readily apparent that on a Bode phase plot the 90° phase shift of a lag occurs approximately linearly over a frequency span of about 100 to 1. By contrast, the transition in the slope of the gain function occurs in a frequency span of only about 4 to 1 around the cutoff frequency. One explanation of the disparity was given in connection with Eq. (3.8), and another explanation involving Bode's weighting function is given in Chap 5.

Outstanding Features of Bode Plots

This is a good place to summarize the several outstanding desirable features of Bode plots as illustrated by the first example. The log gain and frequency scales allow a great range of the variables to be displayed without running off the graph or suffering loss of detail at one end or the other. The phase characteristics are symmetrical about break frequencies; they are also identical, except for polarity in some instances, for each independent energy storage element. The cascading of networks requires only simple addition of phase and log gain.

Some of these points are illustrated graphically in Fig. 4-2, which shows closed-loop gain as a function of frequency for a typical feedback system. With either log or linear scales on both the x and the y axes possible, four combinations exist, and it is obvious that the log-log combination of the Bode plot, in the upper-right quadrant, gives the most satisfactory presentation. Most of the data is reduced to two straight lines.

Bode Plots for Other Networks

The remainder of this chapter develops Bode plots for several other common elements. Although few in number, when suitably combined, they describe with adequate accuracy a surprisingly high fraction of actual feedback loops. For some we repeat the procedure used with the lag network, which, to review, involves the following steps:

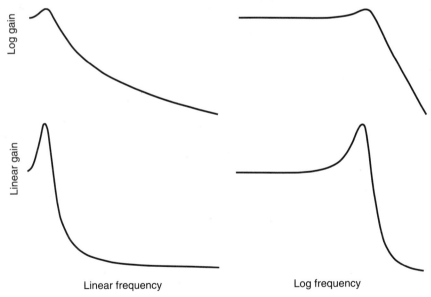

Figure 4-2. An arbitrary gain versus frequency characteristic plotted four ways.

1. Start with the schematic.

2. Express reactances in the frequency domain.

3. Write the frequency domain transfer function with the aid of Ohm's law and Kirchhoff's laws.

4. Convert the transfer function into polar form, i.e., gain and phase.

5. Convert the gain to decibels.

6. Plot asymptotes for both decibels and phase against log frequency.

7. Round the curves near breakpoints if desired.

Although this list might look formidable, the steps are all so simple that the entire process is quite easy for simple circuits. Where several networks are cascaded and the composite transfer function is somewhat complicated, combining the Bode plots of the individual components to get the composite Bode plot is usually easier than working from the composite transfer function.

Looking first at an integrator, which gives an output proportional to the time integral of the input, we have Eq. (4.3).

$$e_o = \int e_i dt \qquad\qquad (4.3)$$

With $e_i = \sin \omega t$ Eq. (4.3) becomes Eq. (4.4).

$$\begin{aligned}
e_o &= \int \sin \omega t \, dt \qquad\qquad (4.4)\\
&= -(1/\omega)\cos \omega t\\
&= (-j/\omega)\sin \omega t\\
&= (-j/\omega)e_i\\
&= (1/\omega)e_i / \underline{-90°}
\end{aligned}$$

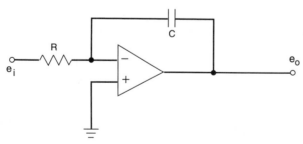

Figure 4-3. An op amp–based circuit that integrates and inverts a signal.

Thus the transfer function is

$$w = e_o/e_i$$
$$= (-j)/\omega \tag{4.5}$$
$$= 1/(j\omega)$$

Here the proportionality constant is unity. When an integrator is implemented electronically with an op amp, as in Fig. 4-3, the voltage gain, which is the same thing as the transfer function, can be written down by inspection, as we discuss in more detail in Chap. 13 on op amps.

$$w = -X_c/R$$
$$= -1/(j\omega RC) \tag{4.6}$$
$$= -1/(j\omega T)$$

The minus sign is the result of inversion by the circuit, not the integration. As in the lag network, the RC product, which has the dimensions of time, is called the *time constant*, denoted by T. It is the proportionality constant for the integrator and, as is the case for the lag network, is the sole parameter that is variable. It is interesting that the time constant, relating to frequency, serves equally well as a gain constant. This condition results from the fact that on a Bode plot the gain curve is a straight line with constant slope forever so that moving it sideways is indistinguishable from moving it up or down.

The transfer function for an integrator is so simple that it is in polar form immediately, showing that the phase lags by 90° at all frequencies and that the slope is -6 dB/octave at all frequencies. The gain goes through unity, or 0 dB, when $\omega T = 1$ at the frequency $f = 1/(2\pi T)$. Above the break frequency of a lag with the same time constant, the Bode plots of the two are identical. Below the break frequency of the lag, the gain of the integrator continues to increase as the frequency decreases, approaching infinity as the frequency approaches zero. For this reason integrators were occasionally put in feedback loops deliberately to reduce the steady-state error, as seen in Eq. (2.1) to zero. This approach is seldom necessary or desirable now, as we will see in Chap. 14, but integrators are still encountered, most commonly when a motor moves something and position is the variable of interest, when a voltage-to-frequency converter drives a counter, or when a voltage-controlled oscillator is used in a phase-locked loop.

It is almost intuitively obvious that a differentiator will have opposite characteristics, that is, a slope of 6 dB/octave and a phase lead of 90° at all frequencies. However, we will not bother to show this situation, since real differentiators are seldom encountered, and they cannot, of course, maintain the theoretical characteristic indefinitely as frequency increases, because no real component can have infinite gainbandwidth product. In general, differentiators should be shunned because they amplify high-frequency noise excessively. The Bode gain and phase plots for both an integrator and a differentiator, as just described, are so simple that figures would be superfluous.

Next we consider two networks that are opposites, in a sense, like the integrator and differentiator, but unlike that pair, these networks are both of great importance to feedback theory. They are the phase retard and phase advance networks, to use Thomason's terminology (Thomason, 1955, p. 215). Incidentally, occasionally in feedback literature phase retard networks are referred to as *lags,* but a distinction needs to be maintained. The schematic for the phase retard network appears in Fig. 4-4. It is identical to the lag network except for the addition of $R2$. The transfer function is somewhat more complicated, but if $R2$ is much less than $R1$, we can easily draw the Bode plots directly. They will be the same as for a lag with time constant $T = R1C$ at low and moderate frequencies, but ultimately as the frequency increases and the reactance of the capacitor becomes negligible compared to $R2$, the circuit becomes just a simple voltage divider with gain $R2/(R1 + R2)$ and the phase shift returns to zero. The magnitude of the attenuation, which is the reciprocal of the gain, is the factor by which the second break frequency is higher than the first. Bode plots for attenuations of 20 dB and 60 dB appear in Fig. 4-5. If the two break frequencies are only a factor of 10 apart, with 20 dB attenuation, the rounded-off phase curve becomes an inverted hump that reaches a peak of only about 55°, rather than 90°. For higher attenuation, 90° is approached quite closely.

A phase advance network appears in Fig. 4-6. This network becomes a voltage divider at very low frequencies and has unity gain at very high frequencies, with a transition between them, just as with the

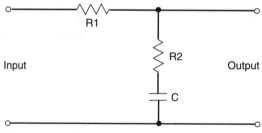

Figure 4-4. Phase retard network.

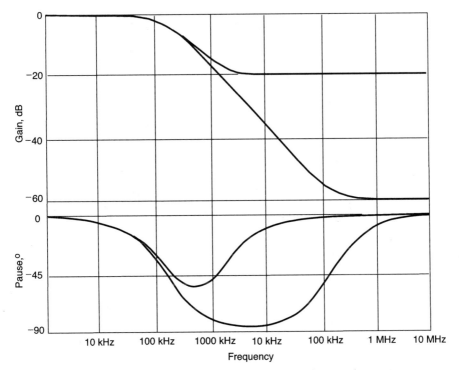

Figure 4-5. Bode gain and phase plots for a phase retard network.

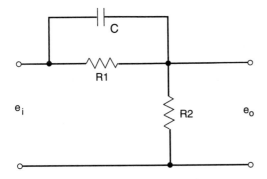

Figure 4-6. Phase advance network.

phase retard network. The time constant of the lower break frequency is $R1C$, and the ratio of break frequencies is the reciprocal of the attenuation, resulting in the Bode plots of Fig. 4-7.

Now we will consider a few combinations of components, starting with two cascaded lags having identical time constants and shown in Fig. 4-8. We have shown a unity gain buffer between the two lags to eliminate loading of the first by the second. Alternatively, the impedance values of the second lag could be much higher than those of the first. The decibels and phase at every frequency are simply doubled, resulting in asymptotes of −12 dB/octave and 180° of phase shift at frequencies above the break frequency. The Bode gain plot appears in Fig. 4-9. Starting here, we dispense with the phase curve for minimum phase components, and for the most part we will not bother to round

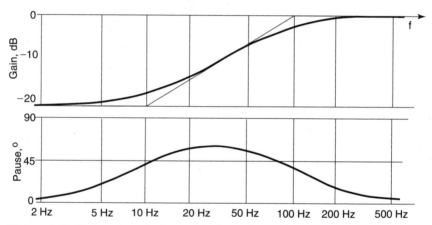

Figure 4-7. Bode gain and phase plots for a phase advance network.

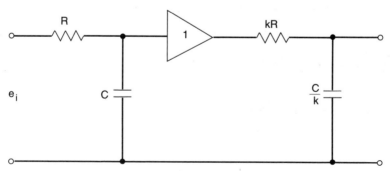

Figure 4-8. Cascaded lag networks with buffering.

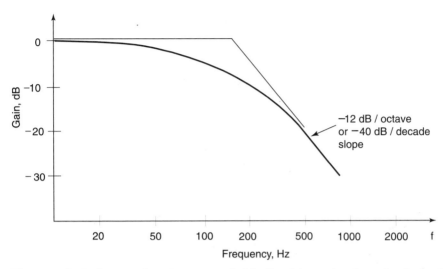

Figure 4-9. Bode gain plot of two cascaded buffered lag networks with identical time constants.

curves subsequently. The figures will then look like those ordinarily made on the job. Two cascaded lags with different break frequencies result in the plot of Fig. 4-10.

Next we consider a combination of a lag and a phase retard network with the upper break frequency of the phase retard network equal to the break frequency of the lag network. This requires that $R2C$ for the phase advance network equal RC for the lag. The two component gain curves and the composite characteristic in Fig. 4-11 show that with these values, the composite curve has exactly the same characteristics as a lag network alone, with an exception; the time constant is

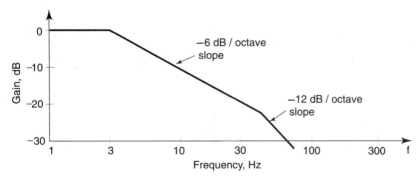

Figure 4-10. Bode gain plot of two cascaded buffered lag networks with different time constants.

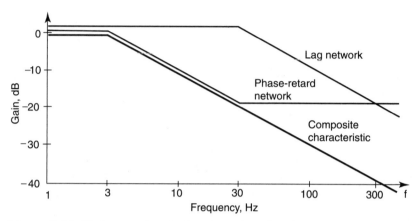

Figure 4-11. Bode gain plot of a lag network and a phase retard network in series.

increased and the break frequency is decreased by the attenuation factor of the phase retard network, 10, or 20 dB, in this example. For the sake of clarity, the curves are slightly displaced from their true value at places where two or more virtually coincide.

A combination of a lag and a phase advance network, with the lower break frequency of the phase advance network identical to the break frequency of the lag network, appears in Fig. 4-12. As in the preceding example, the composite characteristic is identical to that of a lag alone,

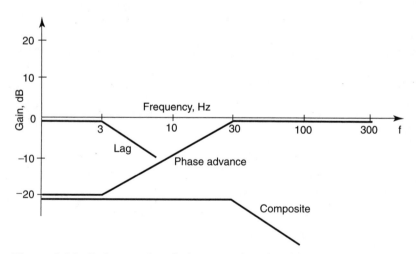

Figure 4-12. Bode gain plot of a lag network and a phase advance network in series.

but in this case the time constant for the combination is decreased and the break frequency increased by the attenuation factor. Also, the gain is attenuated 20 dB. Both of these last two combinations are widely used when compensating loops, as discussed in detail in Chap. 10.

Another frequently encountered combination comprises two lags with different time constants and a phase advance network that cuts in at the break frequency of the lag with the higher break frequency, as shown in Fig. 4-13. It is evident that, compared to the gain of the two cascaded lags alone, the phase advance network has significantly increased the frequency at which the composite slope goes from -6 to -12 dB/octave, and the phase from $-90°$ to $-180°$.

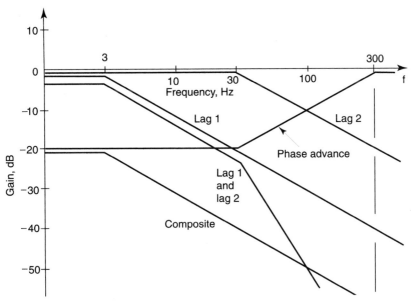

Figure 4-13. Bode plot of two lag networks and a phase advance network in series.

5

Bode's Weighting Function

A bank is a place that will give you a loan if you can prove you don't need it, according to an old saying. Bode's weighting function is a little bit similar in that it will give you the phase function from the gain function, but only for minimum phase networks, and for these you really don't need the phase function. This situation is an inevitable and logical consequence of the fact that if it is possible to get the phase function from the gain function, the former cannot contain any additional information and the redundancy may complicate use of the information while contributing little if any increase in convenience. Nevertheless, for several reasons that will become apparent as we progress, Bode's weighting function is of considerable theoretical and practical importance, so we will devote a brief chapter to it.

Minimum Phase Networks

This discussion depends on the important fact that every gain characteristic has a minimum phase characteristic that no physically realizable network can get under, although it is entirely possible for the phase to exceed the theoretical minimum. That there is a minimum can be surmised from reflecting on the several networks studied in Chaps. 3 and 4. All except the phase advance network provide attenuation as the frequency increases, but with concomitant phase shift. This condition raises the question of whether we can achieve comparable attenuation without any phase shift at all. Such a circuit would be so useful that anyone who could invent and patent it would be on easy street. However, the fact that no one has ever developed this circuit strongly suggests that it is impossible, meaning that a minimum phase function somewhat above zero exists for the gain characteristics studied so far, as has been demonstrated theoretically by Bode in Chap. 13 of his classic work (Bode, 1945).

Consequently, all networks can be divided into two mutually exclusive categories, *minimum phase networks* (MPNs) and nonMPNs. All networks in the latter category will have phase shift in all or part of the frequency spectrum greater than the phase shift of an MPN with an identical gain versus frequency curve. The phase characteristic can be calculated from the gain characteristic for MPNs only, since the phase of a non-MPN can be increased arbitrarily with delay lines and other circuits, which we consider shortly, without altering the gain characteristic.

Determining Phase from Gain for an MPN

Calculation of the phase at an arbitrary frequency f_c for an MPN can be effected with Eq. (5.1), developed by Bode (1945, p. 313).

$$\phi_c = \frac{1}{\pi} \int_{-\infty}^{\infty} \left(\frac{dA}{du} \right) \ln \coth \mid \frac{u}{2} \mid du \qquad (5.1)$$

Here ϕ_c is the phase in radians at frequency c, A is the logarithmic gain as a function of frequency, $u = \ln(f/f_c)$, and ln is used to denote natural log, that is, log to the base ϵ, instead of log to the base 10, which is used for decibels. To get the phase at any one frequency, it is necessary to carry out the integration over the entire frequency spectrum, with f going from 0 to ∞, so that u goes from $-\infty$ to $+\infty$. If Eq. (5.1) looks a bit intimidating, we hasten to point out that we will never need to do even a single integration to find the phase at one frequency, let alone many to determine a complete phase curve.

Two important features of Eq. (5.1) stand out upon inspection. The first is that the phase at frequency c depends on the slope dA/du of the gain characteristic as it appears on a Bode plot, rather than on the gain itself. This feature correlates with something you probably noticed in the preceding chapter—that the phase was always proportional to the slope except for slight deviations in the vicinity of break frequencies. The second feature is that the integral describes a low-pass filtering operation of dA/du, using ln coth$|u/2|$ as a weighting function. The filtering operation is very similar to taking a running average, for example, which is another low-pass filtering, or smoothing, operation. The difference is that when taking a running average, all the points over which the average is taken are weighted equally so that the weighting function is rectangular. The filtering operation involves centering the weighting function at the point where a filtered value is desired, multiplying the two functions point by point, summing the products, and dividing by the number of points to get the average value over the interval covered by the weighting function. The weighting function is then shifted, and the whole operation is repeated to get the next filtered value, and so on to get the entire filtered function. The reason the multiplication and summing doesn't need to be carried out from $-\infty$ to $+\infty$ for a running average is that the products are zero outside of the span of the weighting function in that case.

This explanation of a running average applies to discrete data, as in a digital computer, and is a little simpler than the explanation of a continuous process that involves integration instead of summing. The basic idea and results, however, are essentially the same for both.

Other weighting functions, or *kernels* as they are sometimes called, provide different types of filtering. A pyramid shape is sometimes used, or a decaying exponential reversed with respect to time. The latter gives a filtering action identical to that produced by a simple RC section, or lag network, as can be verified by shifting the function from left to right through a step function. Bode's weighting function is used only when the function to be filtered is the slope of a logarithmic gain function. The unfiltered slope is an approximation to the minimum phase possible for that gain characteristic, and the filtering makes it exact.

Features of Bode's Weighting Function

The weighting function in Eq. (5.1), ln coth $|u/2|$, is called *Bode's weighting function* and is shown graphically in Fig. 5-1. Salient features are its symmetry on a log frequency scale, that it goes to infinity at the center, and that the bulk of the weighting is confined to a range from about one-third to three times the frequency at which the phase is being calculated. Values of f/f_c along the horizontal axis of Fig. 5-1 emphasize this relationship. Thus the slope of the logarithmic gain characteristic at and quite near the frequency where the phase is being

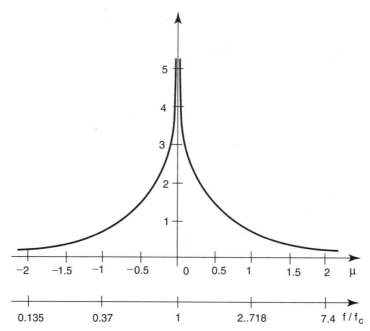

Figure 5-1. Bode's weighting function, ln coth $|u2|$.

calculated is weighted far more heavily than the values at significantly higher and lower frequencies. The infinite value of the weighting function at its center might suggest that the slope there would determine the phase all by itself, but this is not quite the case because the weighting function gets so narrow as it goes to infinity. Nevertheless, the phase will usually be close enough to the value based on the slope at the center of the weighting function that we will often use that value to avoid having to use Eq. (5.1). The calculations would be impractical for the quick and dirty approximations needed when dealing with ordinary feedback loops, whether attempted analytically, graphically, or by numerical integration, even with the aid of a computer.

Despite the concentration of weighting near the center of the function, unusually steep slopes of the gain characteristic can still cause significant phase shift far away as a result of the tails of the function. We will look at this topic further in Chap. 6.

In the previous chapter we mentioned that most of the transition from a slope of 0 dB/octave to a slope of -6 dB/octave for a lag network takes place over a frequency span of about 4 to 1. However, as noted earlier the effect of the filtering is to make the phase transition substantially broader. This effect is a consequence of the considerable frequency span over which Bode's weighting function has significant amplitude. By keeping the scale of the smoothing effect of Eq. (5.1) on a lag network in mind, we can do a pretty good job of estimating the phase of any MPN, given the gain curve. That approach is a lot easier than using Bode' equation.

Applications

One of the values of Bode's weighting function, as used in Eq. (5.1), is that it provides a means for determining whether experimental data came from an MPN or not. The phase function calculated from the experimental gain function is compared to the experimental phase function, and if the latter is greater at some frequencies, the network is not an MPN. If the experimental phase is less, then either the experimental gain data or phase data, or both, are defective.

A more sophisticated application of this concept would be looking for transmission delay in a neural system. The system might have features such as memory or pattern recognition capability which would compromise the validity of measurements made with repetitive inputs, including sine waves. Consequently, it would be desirable to use a random or pseudorandom test input and to cross correlate this data with the output to yield the time domain delta function response of the system, as suggested by Lee (1950). Any delay would be more or less evident in this signal, but reading it off accurately might be difficult if the delay were quite short and if the response, aside from the effect of the delay, took off rather slowly. To obviate this difficulty, the delta function response could be Fourier-transformed to give gain and phase functions (Weaver, 1983, p. 156) that could be processed as just discussed. If the difference between the experimental and calculated phases, on a linear frequency scale, could be fit quite accurately with a straight line, the slope of the line would be proportional to a transmission delay, as we will see in Chap. 6, and the quality of the fit would provide a measure of the confidence that could be attached to the value. In addition, a positive zero offset would indicate hysteresis, as will be explained in Chap. 6. The amplitude spectrum allows the system time constants to be determined using the method discussed in Chap. 11. The higher the accuracy required, the longer the data set needed. Fortunately most computers and processing programs can now handle very long data sets, which is necessary in several contexts.

This activity would presumably take place in a research laboratory with a computer performing all the operations, including generating a pseudorandom test signal, performing cross correlation, calculating

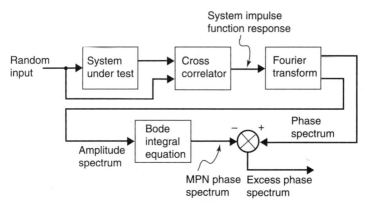

Figure 5-2. Test setup for measuring system time delay.

the minimum phase, and doing the curve fitting, so the apparent complexity would not be a serious problem. The signal-processing functions appear in block diagram form in Fig. 5-2. Various inputs and outputs are feasible. If the system being tested is a human being and eye-hand coordination is the function of interest, the input might be a spot moving back and forth horizontally on a computer monitor, with the output being the position of the cursor repeating the position of the mouse moved by the subject's hand. The transfer function of the mouse, if not essentially unity, would have to be taken into account.

Interesting as such applications of Bode's weighting function are, they are straying away from our main concern, so we will conclude the chapter at this point with a summary. The phase of MPNs can be determined from the complete gain characteristic; phase is approximately proportional to the slope of the gain characteristic as it appears on a Bode plot; the proportionality constant is 90° for each 6 dB/octave slope; and filtering the slope with Bode's weighting function yields the exact phase at all frequencies.

6
Excess Phase

Excess phase from nonminimum phase components degrades the performance of feedback loops, so it is important to have means to identify non-MPN elements and to exclude them if at all possible. The designer who does so will also be able to use the simpler and easier analysis techniques that are valid only for MPN loops. Fortunately, several clues help to identify non-MPN components. First, if experimental data is available, the method discussed at the end of Chap. 5 can be used. This method can usually be simplified by comparing the measured phase with the minimum phase, based on the gain characteristic at just a few frequencies where the slope of the gain characteristic is nearly uniform for a considerable distance in both directions. At such points the minimum phase will be very close to 15° for each decibel per octave of slope, obviating the need to use Eq. (5.1).

Sources of Excess Phase

The distinction can also be based on structure. All ladder networks, such as the one shown in Fig. 6-1, are MPNs. Each box can be resistance, capacitance, or inductance, or a series or parallel combinations of those elements. They can also be analogous mechanical or other elements. On the other hand, lattice networks and bridged structures, such as a twin tee or bridged tee, are not MPNs. Examples are shown in Fig. 6-2. The feature of these network types that creates a potential for excess phase is multiple pathways from the input to the output. Several components in series or parallel between two nodes are all right so long as they do not leapfrog an intermediate node, as in bridged structures. Strictly applied, this criterion puts transistors in

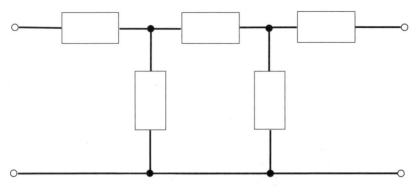

Figure 6-1. Ladder network.

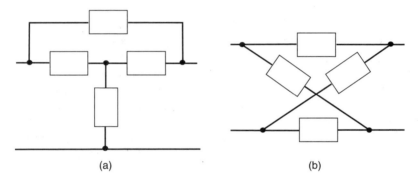

(a)   (b)

Figure 6-2. (a) Bridged tee and (b) lattice networks.

the common emitter configuration into the non-MPN classification because of collector-to-base capacitance. Fortunately, however, for most transistors the excess phase will be negligible around the unity gain frequency of typical feedback loops.

If a lattice or bridge structure is purely resistive, it will introduce no phase shift at all and hence no excess phase. However, this case seldom occurs when reactances are involved. A classic case is a lattice used as an all-pass network to linearize the phase of a filter by introducing phase shift where needed, but without changing the attenuation characteristic. Since the minimum phase of a flat attenuation characteristic is zero, all the phase of the lattice is excess and it must be substantial in order to be useful.

Another clue to a nonminimum phase component is that its initial step function response is of the opposite polarity to the final response, as shown in Fig. 6-3. Such a response indicates the existence of multi-

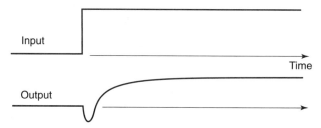

Figure 6-3. Step function response indicating a nonminimum phase transfer function.

ple pathways from the input to the output, with one dominating initially and a different one taking over later.

For those who also work with s-plane transfer functions, any zeroes in the right half plane indicate a nonminimum phase transfer function.

Yet another source of excess phase is hysteresis, which occurs when the input/output relationship of a component depends on the direction the input is changing. Common sources include backlash in gear trains; complementary emitter followers with a reactive component of load; and iron-cored components such as transformers, some motors, and *linear variable differential transformer* (LVDT) type transducers. Hysteresis is a nonlinearity, which strictly speaking, should not be allowed, but considerable tolerance of nonlinearities in the forward path is commonplace, since feedback reduces their effect. A typical curve for an iron-cored device appears in Fig. 6-4. It introduces a phase shift in the output as shown in Fig. 6-5 without any associated frequency-dependent attenuation, so this is excess phase. Since the excess phase is independent of frequency, it does not become enormous at high frequencies, but neither does it become negligible at low frequencies. The amount of excess phase is, however, a function of signal level.

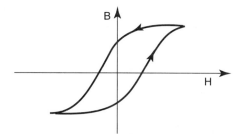

Figure 6-4. Hysteresis curve of ferromagnetic material.

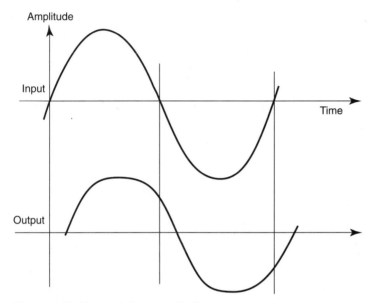

Figure 6-5. Phase shift caused by hysteresis.

The most common source of excess phase is a delay, or transport lag. Figure 6-6 shows that the phase shift in degrees is to the delay τ as $360°$ is to the period of one cycle $1/f$. Therefore,

$$\phi = (360)\tau f \tag{6.1}$$

The phase varies linearly with frequency, which is good when it relates to a phase linear filter, meaning that the filter delays, but does not distort, a waveform. In a feedback loop, however, this condition is bad because there is no associated attenuation, so it is pure excess phase, which has a serious destabilizing effect.

Equivalent Excess Phase

The preceding description applies to a pure delay generated by a theoretically ideal delay line. A real lumped parameter delay line consisting of many LC sections is shown, except for terminating sections at each end, in Fig. 6-7. Since this delay line is obviously a ladder network, it raises an interesting question. How can a ladder network, which is an MPN, generate the excess phase of a delay? The explanation is simply that while a lumped parameter delay line generates delay, and hence phase shift proportional to the delay and to the frequency, the phase is

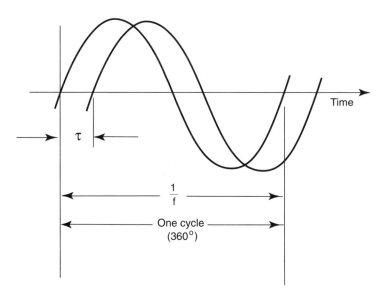

Figure 6-6. Phase shift caused by transport lag or delay.

not excess relative to the complete attenuation characteristic of the line. At some frequency far above the signal spectrum the line is designed to handle, each section starts to act as a low-pass filter, and because there are a great many sections, the attenuation above the cutoff frequency is extremely steep. The steep slope, in conjunction with the tail of Bode's weighting function, generates the phase shift at low frequencies.

Since no one would deliberately put a delay line of any type in a feedback loop, this information is of limited direct significance, but it leads to a consideration of some related conditions that do occur frequently. One is the presence in a loop of a number of lags with break frequencies so far above the unity gain crossover frequency that there is a tendency to ignore them. However, each lag generates phase shift $\phi = \tan^{-1}\omega T$. At frequencies far below the cutoff frequency of the lag, ωT is very small and the inverse tangent function is essentially the

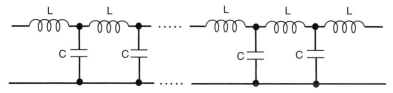

Figure 6-7. Lumped parameter delay line.

same as its argument. Therefore $\phi = \omega T$ rad, or $360fT°$, where T is the time constant of the lag. Thus, we derive exactly the same phase function produced by a pure delay of time T, so the time constants of all the high-frequency lags can be added up to give an equivalent transport lag, even though the lag networks are MPNs. The resulting phase shift might well be called "equivalent excess phase" since it is not, strictly speaking, excess at all.

These short time constants are often introduced by unity gain buffers that eliminate loading effects. Fortunately, the so-called video buffers now available have time constants so short that several of them added up usually will not produce a troublesome amount of equivalent excess phase.

Another related condition is heat flow by conduction, or thermal diffusion. A lumped parameter model of diffusion is similar to a lumped parameter delay line except with RC sections instead of with LC sections. The transfer function of each section is similar to, but not exactly, that given by Eq. (3.6) because of loading by the remainder of the line, leading to excess phase, or at least to equivalent excess phase, as just discussed. To minimize excess phase, the heat source and the temperature sensor in a temperature control loop should be as close together as possible. In addition, small sensors are desirable to minimize the time for a change in temperature to propagate from the surface of the sensor to the active element.

Excess Phase on Bode Plots

Since the phase of a delay is linear with frequency, the shape on a Bode phase plot is exponential. Curves for two values of delay, differing by a factor of two, appear in Fig. 6-8, along with the phase curve of a lag

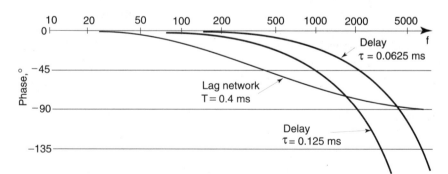

Figure 6-8. Linear phase shift plotted on a log frequency scale.

for comparison. The most obvious feature is a frequency below which the shift for a given delay is completely negligible, while the shift increases rapidly above that frequency. In one sense that frequency is arbitrary, since it can be moved at will by changing the y-axis scaling. However, since the y axis for a typical Bode phase plot usually needs to encompass about 200°, the frequency at which the phase takes off is actually fairly well fixed. In other words, the takeoff frequency occurs when the phase shift becomes significant, say, 5° or 10°.

Common sources of delay are discussed in Chap. 16.

7

Transducers

Actuators

Frequently the controlled variable is something other than a voltage, examples being velocity, position, temperature, and light intensity. If the gain in the loop is obtained electrically, devices are needed to convert between voltage and the desired controlled variable. Such devices are called *transducers,* and two of them are needed for a loop. The first, at the output end of the *A* path, converts the amplified electrical signal to the desired output, and its dynamic characteristics are included in the overall Bode plot for the *A* path. Transducers used for this purpose are frequently called *actuators.* Examples of actuators for the controlled variables mentioned above are motors, heaters, and light bulbs. Feedback can markedly improve any deficiencies they have in regard to linearity, frequency response, and the like.

Sensors

A second transducer converts the value of the controlled variable back to a voltage to be fed to the loop comparator. Transducers used for this purpose are commonly called *sensors.* In some instances the same transducer can be used either as an actuator or as a sensor, the direction of signal flow through it being opposite for the two cases. Examples of sensors include tachometers, potentiometers, thermistors, and photodiodes. Unfortunately, feedback cannot mitigate all the deficiencies of a transducer when it is used as a sensor. The accuracy with which feedback can control a variable obviously cannot exceed the accuracy with which its value can be sensed.

The Bode plot for the B path must include the dynamic characteristics of sensors. Because we largely ignore this complication in our analysis, any resonances or nonlinearities of sensors below the crossover frequency should be flattened out with local compensation if at all possible. B should be flat with frequency in order that $1/B$, the closed-loop gain, will be flat also. We touch on this topic again in Chap. 11 in connection with loop compensation.

Electric Motors

The subject of transducers is far too complex and extensive to cover thoroughly here; entire books are devoted to electromechanical devices alone (Del Toro, 1968). However, transducers, particularly motors, are too important to skip completely. Two-phase induction motors have been used in ac servo systems where requirements are not too exacting, such as in chart-recorder mechanisms. However, the superior characteristics of motors with ceramic permanent magnet fields and moving-coil armatures are needed for high-performance systems, and we will confine our brief discussion of motors to this type. They have many outstanding features. The armature consists solely of wire in a basket wound configuration, resulting in minimal inertia for snappy acceleration. A stationary iron core inside the armature for the magnetic return path contributes no inertia and no magnetic hysteresis, since the flux there is constant. The absence of hysteresis reduces losses and eliminates a possible source of excess phase. The ceramic permanent magnet field confers several additional advantages compared to a motor with a shunt wound field. The motor can be smaller for a given rating, another source of losses is eliminated, and a power supply for field excitation is unnecessary. Much more important, the low permeability of ceramic magnets greatly reduces armature reaction, leading to better commutation (less sparking at the brushes) and a more linear current-torque characteristic, especially at high currents, resulting in higher maximum torque, which allows superior acceleration. However, it is well to limit the peak current to about seven times the rated continuous current of the motor to avoid undue risk of demagnetizing the field.

The transfer function depends on whether one considers current or voltage as the input, and torque, velocity, or angle as the output. When the input is current and the output is torque, Lenz's law causes a highly linear relationship and the device is called a *torque motor*. For this case the transfer function is simply a proportionality constant if the torque developed by the winding is considered as the output. If the output is taken as the torque in the shaft to the load, it will differ from the winding torque when there is acceleration because some of the winding torque will be used internally to accelerate the inertia of the armature. However, in this instance it is ideal to handle the effect of loading by simply combining the load and the motor into one, by adding the armature and load inertias. This approach is ideal because the two inertias are not independent energy storage elements. However, if the load is geared down, the relative contributions will have to be weighted by the square of the reduction ratio, since energy storage varies as the square of velocity. Usually nothing can be done about the load inertia, but it is well to avoid very high reduction ratios that may cause an excessive increase in the total because the armature inertia is weighted so heavily.

In many cases the input is voltage, and the output is the velocity of rotation. In this mode the motor itself is a feedback loop, since the armature generates a back emf, just as if it were a speed-sensing tachometer. As the motor picks up speed, its back emf will subtract from the applied voltage, reducing the current to just enough to drive the load at constant speed with no torque left over for acceleration. The mechanical time constant T_M is proportional to the inertia of the armature and load and inversely proportional to the torque developed per unit current. The mechanical time constant enters into the transfer function as the time constant of a lag.

In addition, an electrical time constant is determined by the series combination of the resistance R and the inductive reactance $j\omega L$ of the armature winding. Then

$$i = e/(R + j\omega L)$$

or

$$i/e = (1/R)/(1 + j\omega L/R) \qquad (7.1)$$

The electrical time constant T_E is equal to L/R. It will usually be much shorter than T_M, so the transient response due to the electrical time constant will usually be essentially complete before the speed changes much. Therefore, simply cascading the two lags results in a good approximation of the composite transfer function in Eq. (7.2).

$$w(j\omega) = \psi/e = K/[(1 + j\omega T_E)(1 + j\omega T_M)] \qquad (7.2)$$

Here we are using ψ for the angular velocity of the motor, rather than the usual ω, because we use ω throughout the book for the angular velocity of the input sinusoid. The constant K is the steady-state motor speed per unit voltage.

The time integral of velocity is position, so when position is the output, an integrator transfer function must also be included, giving Eq. (7.3).

$$w(j\omega) = \theta/e = 1/[j\omega T_I(1 + j\omega T_E)(1 + j\omega T_M)] \qquad (7.3)$$

Here, angular position is denoted by θ, and the value of K has been consolidated into T_I. Bode plots for the two cases, velocity and position output, appear in Fig. 7-1. These plots are what one normally works with, rather than the transfer functions themselves.

The outstanding performance of this type of motor can seem almost unbelievable. In the test setup shown in Fig. 7-2, the motor is in a loop that controls angular velocity, and a disk with markings is mounted on the shaft to facilitate visual observation of rotation. If the reference input is a bipolar square wave with a frequency of about ½ Hz and

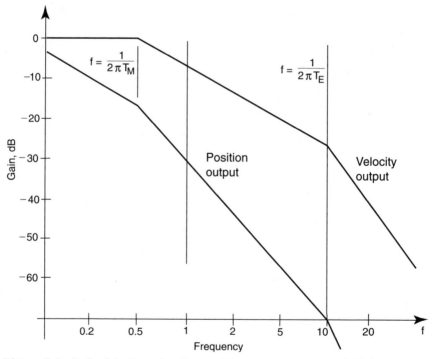

Figure 7-1. Bode plots for a shunt wound or permanent magnet field dc motor.

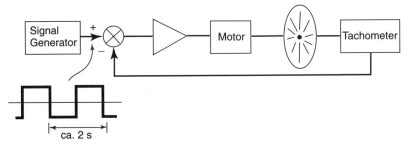

Figure 7-2. Test setup for qualitative evaluation of dc motor performance.

small amplitude, the reversals of direction are easily discernible. When the amplitude of the square wave is increased enough that the velocity of rotation completely blurs the markings on the disk, the only hint that the motor is not operating at constant velocity in one direction is a slight click at the instant of each reversal of direction. Of course, the inertia of the tachometer and any other load must not be excessive.

Even without the feedback the motor could do quite well because it constitutes a feedback loop itself, as mentioned earlier. Figure 7-3 shows the square wave voltage e applied to the motor, the current i, and the angular velocity under these conditions. The electrical time constant has been assumed to be much less than the mechanical time constant, and it is responsible for the rise time of the current at transitions. The large current, as soon as it builds up, results in rapid acceleration to reverse the direction of rotation. As the reversal is accomplished, the current decreases to a low value needed to drive the load

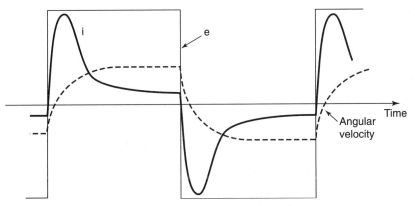

Figure 7-3. Wave forms for dc motor excited with bipolar square wave.

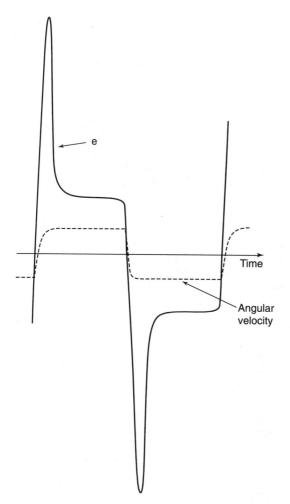

Figure 7-4. Waveforms for dc motor in feedback
loop with bipolar square wave input to loop.

at constant angular velocity. The decrease occurs because the back
electromotive force of the motor approaches the applied voltage.

Figure 7-4 shows the voltage applied to the motor, and angular
velocity, when the motor is in a feedback loop with a gain of four. This
figure shows how the feedback increases response speed in proportion
to the gain by momentarily increasing the voltage applied to the motor
when rapid acceleration is wanted.

Other Transducers

Turning now to sensors, the number of types is so great that we will not attempt to consider any in detail, but will content ourselves with a general discussion. Sensors should be as free as possible from nonlinearity, hysteresis, resonance, excess phase, and long time constants. It is also desirable to have high sensitivity to achieve the necessary high value of A_oB without requiring A_o to be excessively high. Good signal-to-noise ratio is also important.

Electromechanical systems with either linear or angular motion need a way to sense displacement, velocity, or acceleration. In principle, the easiest characteristic to sense could be integrated or differentiated once or twice to determine one of the others if desired. Practically, however, it is usually best to avoid differentiation because of the adverse effect on signal-to-noise ratio. Integration helps in this regard but has a different problem. It gives a value only to within an arbitrary constant, which is seldom satisfactory. Accordingly, the best approach is usually to use a sensor that directly senses the variable that is to be controlled.

If linear displacement is generated by a motor through a screw drive or through a rack and pinion drive, it is usually advantageous to sense the displacement with an angular transducer either on the motor shaft or geared to it. A 10-turn potentiometer or a digital shaft-position encoder driving a digital-to-analog converter are good possibilities, and photoelectric methods have been used to good advantage. Any of these techniques should provide excellent linearity with negligible time constants. Then the contribution of the sensor to the value of B in the loop is just a sensitivity constant.

Another type of displacement sensor that has become much more widely used recently is a television camera with appropriate signal processing. Since the camera samples at the frame rate, however, it is beyond the scope of our treatment of continuous systems.

A linear variable differential transformer is yet another device for measuring displacement, but it has several potential problems. An iron core is usually employed, leading to the possibility of excess phase as a result of hysteresis. In addition, these devices operate by modulating a high-frequency carrier, and the demodulation process used to recover the desired signal also produces an unwanted signal at twice the carrier frequency. This signal is normally removed with a notch filter, usually a twin tee, which can contribute excess phase, as well as introduce an antiresonance into the loop. These problems are usually not too serious because the carrier frequency will be much higher than the system bandwidth, but caution is in order.

A tachometer is the standard device for sensing angular velocity. This small dc generator has a permanent magnet field and thus is essentially the same as a small dc motor. However, when used as a sensor, both the mechanical and electrical time constants can be ignored. The inertia adds to the load inertia, thus affecting the A path transfer function rather than the B path, though usually only to a negligible degree, because the load inertia will usually be much greater than the inertia of the tachometer. As to the electrical time constant, the tachometer will operate into such a high impedance that the current will be virtually zero. Then $L(di/dt)$ must be virtually zero also, so the inductance will not have any retarding effect on the voltage representing angular velocity.

Acceleration is usually sensed with small piezoelectric accelerometers. They will have a resonant peak, but it can usually be made so high that a simple sensitivity constant will suffice for the B path.

For temperature measurement, thermocouples, thermistors, and solid-state sensors are the most used types of sensors. Thermocouples and solid-state sensors have excellent linearity over wide temperature ranges, but have low sensitivity. Thermocouples can be used only in pairs to measure temperature differences, which is fine if that is what is needed but inconvenient if you want an absolute measurement of one temperature. Thermistors, on the other hand, have poor linearity but high sensitivity, and a single thermistor measures absolute temperature. For a regulator the nonlinearity is of little significance, but for other purposes linearity is necessary. A number of analog schemes have been devised to linearize approximately the output of thermistors, and the job now can be done fairly easily and with high accuracy using *digital signal processing* (DSP) or computer techniques. When thermistors are the choice, a few points call for careful attention. Thermistors are usually operated in a bridge, which is a non-MPN circuit. Therefore imbalance of stray capacitances might cause excess phase, as well as introduce a time constant into the loop. Linearization can be done within the loop, right after the thermistor, or by processing the value of the reference input before the loop. The latter has some advantages but allows the incremental loop gain to change with temperature. For a thermistor having a temperature coefficient of -4 percent/°C, the incremental loop gain will change by a factor of 2 over a temperature span of about 18°C. If the operating range is greater than this, it is best to linearize within the loop. The disadvantage is that, if done with DSP, it takes some time, which constitutes a transport lag.

Thermostats, as used in home heating systems, usually utilize a bimetallic strip to open and close a contact. The type of analysis developed for the continuous linear systems considered in this book cannot handle this type of operation.

The optimum light sensor is usually a solid-state photodiode. For linear response with rapid rise time, it is usually operated reverse-biased a few volts, feeding a current-to-voltage converter. The size of the feedback resistor in the converter circuit trades off speed and sensitivity. Extremely high values of either are possible, but not both at the same time, because of the solid-state photodiode's limited gain-bandwidth product. A common solution for this problem is a photo-multiplier tube, which has an extremely high gain-bandwidth product, although it is much bigger, more expensive, and less convenient than photodiodes.

One or two photodiodes can be used with a suitable optical system to make an excellent displacement sensor. Extremely high sensitivity, for small total ranges of displacement, is readily achieved.

For sensing pressure, monolithic solid-state sensors are becoming a good choice.

Chemical sensors such as pH electrodes, ion-specific electrodes, and oxygen sensors are frequently encountered in process control loops. Most of these sensors have a very high internal impedance, meaning that they will probably introduce a significant time constant into the B path, calling for suitable compensation. Furthermore, such sensors are rarely well characterized in this regard, so some experimental work is necessary.

Hydraulic elements constitute an important, but highly specialized, group. We will skip them completely, since they are seldom interfaced to electronic amplification in linear continuous systems, which is our main focus. Computer control of shifting in automatic transmissions has become very common, but also falls outside this field.

Summary

The accuracy of the sensor is the upper limit on the accuracy of the entire loop, and any deficiencies in regard to nonlinearities, resonance, limited bandwidth, and the like should be compensated as far as possible directly following the sensor. The compensated transfer function of the sensor becomes part of the B path transfer function and should be as linear and flat with frequency as possible so that $1/B$, which will be the closed-loop gain, will be linear and flat. The transfer function of actuators becomes part of the A path gain, but feedback can greatly reduce nonlinearities, limited frequency response, low Q resonance, and the like.

8

One-Time-
Constant Loops

After some digression on background material, we are ready to return
to Eq. (2.1) for closed-loop gain, taking into account the frequency
dependence of the forward gain A. In this chapter we will consider
only gain functions with one time constant. This model is too simple to
be realistic for most feedback loops, but it is adequate for a few,
mainly regulators, which are intended to hold an output constant
despite disturbances. The one time constant can be in a lag network or
in an integrator, and we will mention in passing some standard related
nomenclature. Loops are sometimes classified as to order, depending
on the number of time constants, and as to type, depending on the
number of integrators. Thus we will be dealing with first-order loops
(one time constant) of type 0 when a lag network is involved and of
type 1 with an integrator.

Closed-Loop Transfer
Function for First-Order
Type 0 Loop

Starting with the former, the forward gain, or transfer function, will be
the product of a frequency-independent gain A_o and the transfer function of a lag $1/(1+j\omega T)$ in Eq. (8.1).

$$A = A_o/(1 + j\omega T) \qquad (8.1)$$

Inserting Eq. (8.1) into Eq. (2.1) gives the closed-loop gain. We will now call the gain $w(j\omega)$ to emphasize the frequency domain aspect, as shown in Eq. (8.2).

$$w(j\omega) = \frac{1}{B} \frac{1}{(1 + 1/AB)} \tag{8.2}$$

$$= \frac{1}{B} \frac{1}{(1 + 1/A_oB) + j\omega(T/A_oB)}$$

When A_oB is much larger than one, which is necessary for good loop performance, as discussed in Chap. 2, the gain becomes very nearly that shown in Eq. (8.3).

$$w(j\omega) = \frac{1}{B} \frac{1}{1 + j\omega(T/A_oB)} \tag{8.3}$$

Equation (8.3) has the same mathematical form as the forward gain A, namely, a constant times a lag transfer function. However, the constant, which is the low-frequency gain, is $1/B$ instead of A_o, and the effective time constant of the lag has been shortened by the factor A_oB, a large number, thus greatly increasing the cutoff frequency. The gain is constant at low frequencies, never rises above the low-frequency value at any frequency, is 3 dB down from that at the break frequency, which is A_oB/T, and rolls off at 6 dB/octave at higher frequencies forever. These are all known characteristics of a lag network, and the closed-loop gain must have the same characteristics, since it has the same mathematical form.

Features of the Closed-Loop Transfer Function

At high frequencies, above the closed-loop break frequency, the gain becomes essentially $A_o/j\omega T$, with j in the denominator signifying a 90° phase lag. This gain is identical to the high-frequency forward gain. The reason is that the forward gain drops so low that the feedback signal is negligible compared to the input, so it is as if the feedback had been disconnected. This condition must prevail at high frequencies for any open-loop characteristic whatsoever, since the gain of any real forward path must approach zero as the frequency increases indefinitely, due to finite gain-bandwidth product. The ultimate roll-off rate for both forward and closed-loop gains is 6 dB/octave for each independent energy storage element, not counting those in phase advance or retard networks and the like. For the same reasons, the forward path phase and the closed-loop phase also must become identical at high frequencies, approaching 90° for each relevant independent energy storage element. Figure 8-1 shows Bode plots of the forward gain and closed-loop gain of a typical second-order feedback loop superimposed and the forward phase and closed-loop phase superimposed. It is apparent that the forward and closed-loop characteristics are essentially identical above the unity gain frequency.

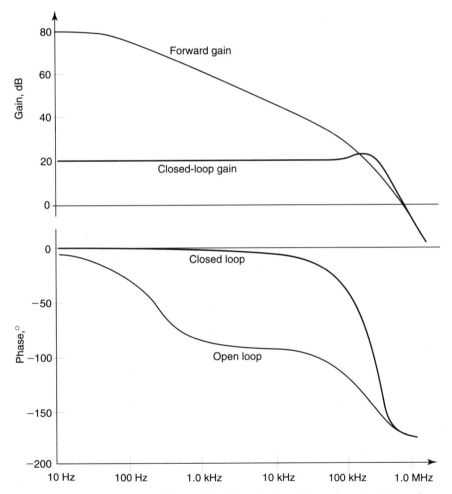

Figure 8-1. Convergence of forward path and closed-loop characteristics above unity gain frequency.

Graphical Analysis

The preceding analytical treatment of this loop is so simple that it might seem unnecessary to draw Bode plots, but we will do so to practice for the more complicated loops to come and because the plots have some features of considerable interest. The following numerical values have been chosen to illustrate a typical situation:

$$A_o = 100,000 \ (100 \ \text{dB})$$
$$B = 1/100 \ (-40 \ \text{dB})$$
$$A_oB = 1000 \ (60 \ \text{dB})$$
$$T = 1 \ \text{ms}$$

Bode plots are shown in Fig. 8-2.

The low-frequency gain is $1/B$, or 40 dB, which is extended until it joins and then follows the forward gain curve A, to give the entire asymptotic closed-loop gain. A feature of interest is that the closed-loop break frequency 160 kHz is the same as the open-loop unity gain crossover frequency, both being $A_oB/2\pi T$. This feature suggests, in a vague way, why peaking, when it occurs under other conditions, is

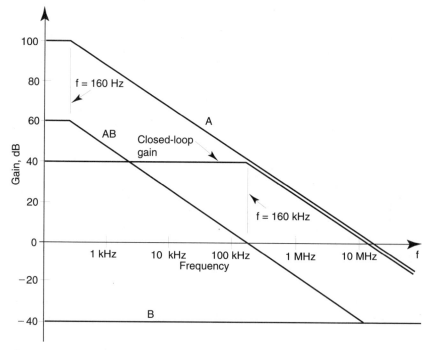

Figure 8-2. Bode plots for feedback loop with one time constant.

near the frequency where roll-off sets in. Oscillation, if it were to occur, would have to be at the open-loop unity gain crossover frequency, so it is plausible to suppose that near oscillation would have to be close to the same frequency, which is also the closed-loop break frequency. Another interesting feature is that the closed-loop gain, although lower than the open-loop gain at low frequencies, exceeds it in the vicinity of the break frequency. This condition reflects the convergence of the closed-loop gain and the forward gain at high frequencies as the feedback dwindles.

Comments about Phase

It is not necessary to consider phase at all, since all elements of the loop are MPNs and therefore the gain curves contain all available information. Otherwise, it would be necessary to use both the gain and phase curves, and the entire problem would not be so simple and easy. It is always well to keep phase in mind, however, and since this is a minimum phase loop, we can infer it from the slope, leading to another feature of interest. The open-loop phase has very nearly reached 90° at the unity gain crossover frequency. This value adds to the 180° introduced by subtracting the feedback signal at the comparator or summing junction, thus giving a total of almost 270° of phase shift around the loop. A phase shift of 360° would bring the feedback signal all the way around to be exactly in phase with the input signal, causing oscillation, so this loop is slightly more than 90° away from that undesirable state of affairs. This cushion is called the *phase margin*. The 90° phase margin is at least sufficient to provide perfect stability in the sense that there is no peaking of the gain versus frequency curve and, as we will see in a moment, no overshoot with a step function input. In fact, a 90° phase margin might be more than enough, but we will defer further consideration until Chap. 16.

Time Domain Characteristics

To complete the analysis of this system, we must ascertain the closed-loop time domain characteristics. These features are usually of more direct interest than the frequency domain characteristics with a few exceptions, such as audio amplifiers. For the sake of simplicity, we focus primarily on just two parameters, rise time and overshoot, when the input is a step function, shown in Fig. 8-3. A theoretically ideal step

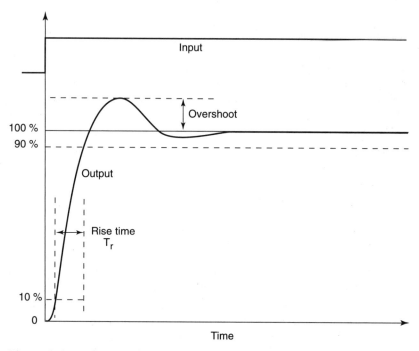

Figure 8-3. Definition of rise time and overshoot.

function has an infinitely fast rise, or zero rise time. Practically, a step function test signal should be at least three times faster than the system under test, but increased speed beyond that will have very little effect on the output. The step function is an excellent test signal for some systems, such as a vertical deflection amplifier for an oscilloscope, which might be used to evaluate the rise time and overshoot of a pulse generator output. The deflection amplifier must have a very fast rise time and essentially no overshoot to accomplish this test satisfactorily and, accordingly, must be tested itself with a very fast step function from a pulse generator. The question of which comes first, the scope or the pulse generator, is reminiscent of the chicken-egg problem, and we will not go into it further. In numerous other situations, step functions are not entirely realistic, the steering problem discussed at the beginning of the book being an example. A step function test in that situation would consist of an abrupt lateral shift of the lane stripes in such a way that the driver had absolutely no advance warning. This shift would probably result in dangerous overcontrol with most cars and drivers because the steering would seem to be too "fast" under these conditions, even though it might be nearly optimum under realistic conditions. We look at this situation a little more at the end of Chap. 16.

In any case the step function, for better or for worse, is the standard test signal for evaluating time domain characteristics, so we return to its use with the loop under discussion. The characteristics can be ascertained directly from Eq. (8.3). Since the transfer function is identical in form to that of a lag network, the response will be identical in shape to that of a lag network, whose response to a step function is known to be

$$e = 1 - \exp(-t/T) \tag{8.4}$$

This curve reaches 63 percent of its final value in one-time-constant T. The rise time, by definition, is the time it takes to get from 10 percent of the final value to 90 percent of the final value, which is 2.2 T for the exponential rise given by Eq. (8.4). Since the effective closed-loop time constant is $T/(A_0 B)$, the closed-loop rise time will be 2.2 $T/A_0 B$, or, with the numerical values used in this example, 2.2 microseconds (μs). No overshoot occurs with Eq. (8.4), so the closed-loop response in this case will also be completely free of overshoot.

If the experimentally observed response of a feedback loop to a step function input has the shape given by Eq. (8.4), and shown in Fig. 8-4, the loop is a first-order system. The characteristic features are a rise that begins without delay, with a slope that jumps from zero to its maximum value at the time of the input step, monotonically decreasing slope thereafter, and asymptotic approach to a constant value.

Closed-Loop Transfer Function of First-Order Type 1 Loop

That completes the analysis of a loop with one lag, so we turn now to a loop with one integrator, a first-order type 1 loop, which is the only other possibility for a loop with only a single time constant. For this type of loop, all the frequency dependence comes from an integrator of time constant T, with all nonfrequency-dependent gain factors in the forward path consolidated into the value of T. Then $A = 1/(j\omega T)$, which can be put in Eq. (2.1) to give Eq. (8.5).

$$w(j\omega) = \frac{1}{B} \frac{1}{1 + j\omega T/B} \tag{8.5}$$

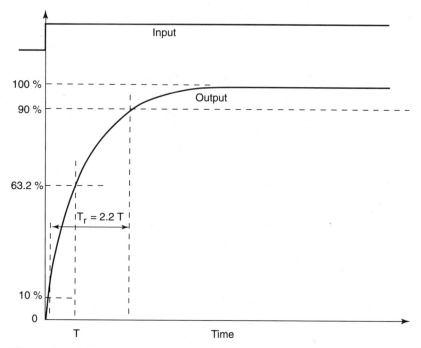

Figure 8-4. Time domain response of lag network with time constant, T.

The zero-frequency gain is exactly $1/B$, and the closed-loop gain curve and step function response curve are the same as the respective curves for a lag network with time constant T/B. Therefore, overshoot and peaking are zero, and the rise time is $2.2T/B$. The Bode plots are the same as for the first-order type 0 loop shown in Fig. 8-1 except that the slope of A and AB continues to the upper-left indefinitely.

If the time constant of the integrator is $1/A_o$ times the time constant of the lag in the type 0 loop, the forward gains will be identical above the break frequency of the lag. The closed-loop gains will be almost identical at all frequencies despite significant differences in the forward and open-loop curves for the two cases at very low frequencies.

9

Two-Time-Constant Loops

Models with two time constants are realistic for more actual feedback loops than the one-time-constant models of the preceding chapter, but they are still an oversimplification for many loops. Nevertheless, two-time-constant models are particularly important because they bring into clear view the cause of instability while being simple enough to allow easy mathematical analysis, thus facilitating heuristic correlation between the mathematical model and physical reality. The intuitive grasp of the situation developed at this level can then be extended, with due caution, to the still more realistic but also more complex models that are not so amenable to exact mathematical analysis. The present chapter can therefore be regarded as the heart of the entire book. Furthermore, some of the traditional concepts of feedback theory with which we want to correlate such as damping factor, relate to second-order systems.

The Cause of Instability

Before turning to equations, a qualitative discussion is in order. With two time constants and plenty of gain, the potential for instability is great, since each time constant can contribute half of the 180° phase shift that, in addition to the 180° introduced at the summing junction, would bring the total around the loop up to 360°, making the feedback positive. The only way to avoid instability is to have the two time constants separated so widely that the longer time constant can attenuate the loop gain to about unity before the second time constant starts to contribute much phase shift adding to the 90° that must accompany the attenuation by the first. Unfortunately, we get little help in the way of attenuation from the shorter time constant, since, as noted in Chap. 3, phase shift sets in well before attenuation as the frequency increases.

Thus we can surmise that the ratio of the two time constants, rather than their values, will be an important parameter and that the ratio must be on the order of the low-frequency loop gain to provide reasonable stability. That is equivalent to saying that the roll-off of the gain with increasing frequency needs to be at −6 dB/octave up to approximately the unity gain frequency. This roll-off can be provided by two lags with widely differing time constants or by one lag and an integrator. If the high-frequency open-loop characteristics of these two possibilities are identical, the closed-loop characteristics will be almost identical also, despite the difference in low-frequency open-loop gain, just as with the type 0 and type 1 first-order loops studied in Chap. 8. Consequently, we complete a detailed analysis only for one, choosing the loop with one lag and an integrator because the math is slightly simpler.

Closed-Loop Transfer Function of Second-Order Type 1 Loop

Bode plots for the loop elements and for the open-loop gain appear in Fig. 9-1. Equation (9.1) gives the forward gain.

$$A = A_o \frac{1}{(j\omega T_1)(1 + j\omega T_2)} \tag{9.1}$$

$$= A_o \frac{1}{-\omega^2 T_1 T_2 + j\omega T_1}$$

A_o could have been consolidated with T_1 so as not to have two parameters serving the same purpose, but keeping both is more convenient when we adapt the results to loops with two lags. A is put into Eq. (2.1) to find the closed loop gain in Eq. (9.2).

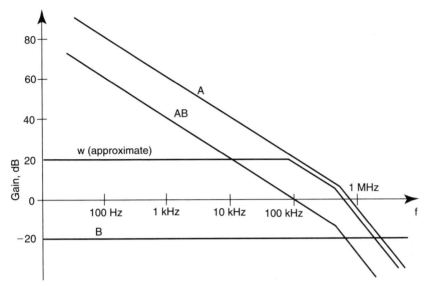

Figure 9-1. Bode plots for feedback loop with two time constants.

$$w(j\omega) = \frac{1}{B}\frac{A_oB}{(A_oB-\omega^2T_1T_2)+j\omega T_1} \tag{9.2}$$

When $\omega = 0$, w is $1/B$ exactly, because the integrator makes the open-loop gain infinite at zero frequency, and at low frequencies the gain is essentially constant at $1/B$ with negligible phase shift. When ω is very high, $w = A_o/(-\omega^2T_1T_2)$, which is identical to A at very high frequencies, for the reason discussed in Chap. 8. The minus sign signifies 180° phase shift, and the gain rolls off at -12 dB/octave because of the appearance of ω^2 as a factor of the denominator. Drawing the asymptotes would give the closed-loop gain curve except for the possibility of a peak near the break frequency. When present, a rise in gain is usually called *peaking*, or sometimes *magnification*, and is expressed as the percent increase in gain over the low-frequency gain. From a mathematical standpoint, this possibility results from the negative term $-\omega^2T_1T_2$ in the denominator, which forces the real component to go through zero at some point as the frequency increases. The negative term is the product of two imaginary numbers resulting from the two time constants and thus was not present in Chap. 8 when only one-time-constant systems were considered.

Peaking

The closed-loop gain and phase characteristics could be obtained from the closed-loop transfer function, Eq. (9.2), by converting it to polar form and evaluating it for a suitable range of values of angular frequency. However, this procedure is much more laborious than necessary, especially since the bulk of the gain characteristic is given simply by the two asymptotes previously mentioned. The only additional information we need is the nature of any peaking that may occur slightly below the closed-loop break frequency. Usually the magnitude of such peaking is of more concern than its exact frequency or shape. The standard way to find a peak or minimum value is to first find the frequency at which it occurs by setting the derivative of the absolute value of the gain with respect to frequency equal to zero, since the slope of the gain will be zero at a peak or minimum. The value of frequency found is then put back into the gain equation to find the peak value.

The math can be simplified somewhat by focusing attention on the denominator of the factor multiplying $1/B$. For convenience we will call it D. See Eq. (9.3).

$$D = A_o B - \omega^2 T_1 T_2 + j\omega T_1 \qquad (9.3)$$

Since the rest of w is real and independent of ω, any peak in the magnitude of w will coincide in frequency with a minimum in the magnitude of the denominator and also, of course, with a minimum in the square of the magnitude of the denominator, which is simpler mathematically. See Eq. (9.4).

$$|D|^2 = (A_o B - \omega^2 T_1 T_2)^2 + (\omega T_1)^2 \qquad (9.4)$$

The components of this function are plotted on linear scales in Fig. 9-2, which is essentially self-explanatory and shows how peaking can occur.

Bearing in mind that the sum of the squares of two numbers is essentially determined by the larger except when they are close, and is simply twice the square of either when they are equal, the magnitude of $|D|^2$ can easily be sketched in approximately. The approximate frequency of a minimum, if any, is also obvious, but we now need to find it exactly by the means just discussed and as shown in Eq. (9.5).

$$\frac{d|D|^2}{d\omega} = 2(A_o B - \omega^2 T_1 T_2)(-2\omega T_1 T_2) + 2\omega T_1^2 \qquad (9.5)$$

$$= 0$$

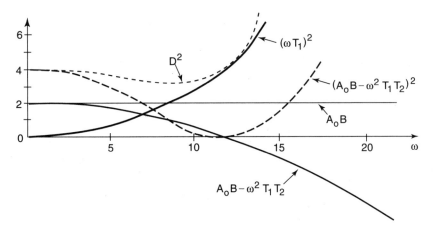

Figure 9-2. Components of the function $|D|^2$ in Eq. (9.4).

From Eq. (9.5) we find Eq. (9.6).

$$\omega^2 = (A_oB)/(T_1T_2) - 1/(2T_2^2) \tag{9.6}$$

Putting this value back in Eq. (9.4) results in quite a few terms, but fortunately most of them cancel out, leaving Eq. (9.7).

$$|D|^2 = A_oB(T_1/T_2) - (1/4)(T_1/T_2)^2 \tag{9.7}$$

To recapitulate, Eq. (9.7) gives the square of the magnitude of the denominator at its minimum if a minimum exists. First let us consider the limiting case of being just on the verge of a minimum. Then the value must be equal to the low-frequency value, which is $(A_oB)^2$ from Eq. (9.4), with $\omega = 0$, as shown in Eq. (9.8).

$$(A_oB)^2 = A_oB(T_1/T_2) - (1/4)(T_1/T_2)^2 \tag{9.8}$$

Using the quadratic formula to solve for T_1/T_2 gives Eq. (9.9).

$$T_1/T_2 = 2A_oB \tag{9.9}$$

The significance of Eq. (9.9) when one of the time constants is due to an integrator is clearer if we look at the Bode plot of Fig. 9-3 and note that the condition of Eq. (9.9) requires the asymptotic gain at the frequency where the slope changes from -6 to -12 dB/octave to be -6 dB.

Next we want to look at peaking for other values of gain at the -6 to -12 dB/octave transition point. When the gain there is 0 dB instead of -6 dB, $T_1/T_2 = A_oB$. Putting this value in Eq. (9.7) gives

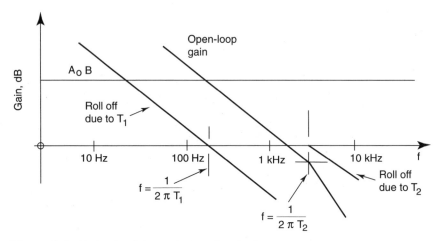

Figure 9-3. Bode plot for type 1 second-order loop.

$$|D|^2 = (A_oB)^2 - (1/4)(A_oB)^2 \qquad (9.10)$$

or

$$|D| = A_oB\sqrt{(3/4)}$$

Since the zero-frequency value of $|D|$ is A_oB, and D is the denominator of the gain, the peaking is $\sqrt{(4/3)} = 1.1547$, or 15 percent above the low-frequency gain. For the case of $+6$ dB gain at the transition point, T_1/T_2 is $(A_oB)/2$, so the gain is $\sqrt{(16/7)} = 1.51$ times the low-frequency gain, or a 51 percent peak. Making similar calculations for a few other values enables us to construct the graph of Fig. 9-4. The x axis also has values of $(T_1/T_2)/(A_oB)$ or $(f_2/f_1)/(A_oB)$, which also determine the peaking, as we will see in a moment. This graph is one of the main objectives of our entire development, providing quantitative information about a principal closed-loop frequency domain performance characteristic from the open-loop gain characteristic alone. The only restriction is that the open-loop characteristic be a minimum phase network, or at least a close approximation to it. This simple relationship between open- and closed-loop characteristics is possible only for such networks, which is one of the two main reasons for exerting every effort to exclude excess phase from feedback loops. The other reason is that excess phase seriously degrades performance.

The frequency of the peak value is slightly below the closed-loop break frequency and is fairly independent of the amount of peaking except for very low values, in which case the frequency of the peak is somewhat lower but nearly irrelevant.

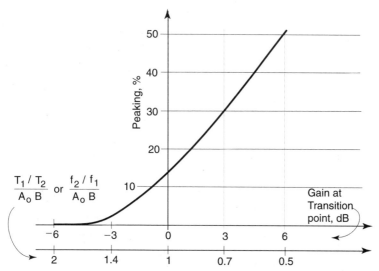

Figure 9-4. Peaking for second-order minimum phase loop as a function of gain at the slope transition point, or as a function of low-frequency gain, and time constants or break frequencies.

Closed-Loop Transfer Function of a Second-Order Type 0 Loop

Logically, we should now turn to the time domain characteristics of two-time-constant loops, but since they cannot be handled as simply as those of one-time-constant loops, we defer that topic to Chap. 12 and take up instead the frequency domain characteristics of loops with two lags. The forward gain is shown in Eq. (9.11).

$$A = A_o \frac{1}{(1 + j\omega T_1)(1 + j\omega T_2)} \tag{9.11}$$

$$= A_o \frac{1}{(1 - \omega^2 T_1 T_2) + j\omega(T_1 + T_2)}$$

Putting Eq. (9.11) into Eq. (2.1) to find the closed-loop gain results in Eq. (9.12).

$$w(j\omega) = \frac{1}{B} \frac{A_oB}{(A_oB + 1 - \omega^2 T_1 T_2) + j\omega(T_1 + T_2)} \qquad (9.12)$$

Equations (9.12) and (9.2), for the closed-loop gain of a loop with one lag and one integrator, are identical in form but have two minor numerical differences. The positive component of the real part of the denominator is $A_oB + 1$ in Eq. (9.12) instead of just A_oB as in Eq. (9.2). This difference is negligible for any useful loop, which must have A_oB much greater than one. The other difference is the appearance of $T_1 + T_2$ in Eq. (9.12) instead of just T_1 in the imaginary part of the denominator. Here again the difference is negligible, since the ratio of time constants must be on the order of A_oB, a large number, to provide reasonable stability. Consequently, the characteristics will be substantially identical except for a minute difference in low-frequency gain, so there is no need to repeat the complete analysis. The peaking will be the same function of the gain at the −6 to −12 dB/octave slope transition.

Stability as a Function of a Simple Ratio

Figure 9-5 shows that since the slope is −6 dB/octave between the two break frequencies, the gain at the second will be just the low-frequency gain divided by the ratio of the time constants, thus providing the basis for the lower scale on the x axis of Fig. 9-4. The main advantage

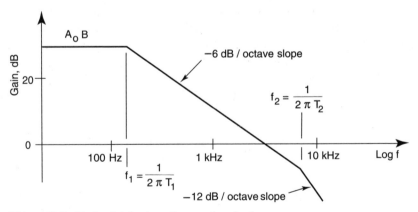

Figure 9-5. Bode plot for type 0 second-order loop.

of this formulation is that it is not necessary to draw or even think about Bode plots. It is by far the simplest and most direct means of finding the peaking for a minimum phase loop with two lags when we know the low-frequency gain and the two time constants or break frequencies.

We will see in Chap. 12 that for second-order systems the overshoot with a step function input can also be given as a graphical function of either the gain at the -6 to -12 dB/octave transition point or the ratio $(T_1/T_2)/(A_oB)$ or $(f_2/f_1)/(A_oB)$. It turns out, not surprisingly, that we can find the overshoot and peaking from several other parameters that we can calculate from A_oB, T_1, and T_2, the principal ones being damping factor and phase margin, which are discussed in Chap 11.

For the relatively rare instances when the slope of the open-loop gain characteristics is steeper than -6 dB/octave, well below the unity gain frequency, design curves are given in Chap. 17.

Conclusion

To conclude this chapter, we mention a few miscellaneous relevant matters. First, the relationships developed do not require any direct concern for phase because for MPNs the phase curve contains no independent information. It is always well to keep phase in mind, but for MPNs it is usually unnecessary, and hence undesirable, to complicate analysis with it.

We can occasionally use Fig. 9-4 to go backward from observed values of peaking to determine one of the time constants, usually the shorter one, if we know the other time constant and the low-frequency open-loop gain.

Third, the effect of the production spread of op amp gains on the open-loop characteristic, especially since only a minimum value is often specified, could be a serious problem. Fortunately, the unity gain frequency rarely has so wide a range of values. As a matter of fact, some op amps, mainly high-frequency types, do not even have the low-frequency gain specified, but only the unity gain frequency. Except for amplifiers with internal feedback to give gains of one or two, we can assume that the gain increases at a 6 dB/octave rate below the unity gain frequency up to at least 10,000 or 100,000. Unusually high gain is accompanied by a lower first break frequency, leaving the midband gain and stability substantially unchanged. In some cases, it is desirable to use a small amount of local feedback around an op amp providing the gain in a larger loop in order to secure a more definite, although lower, gain.

10
Three-Time-Constant Loops

A model with three major time constants is necessary for most of the loops encountered in real life and is also sufficient for the great majority. Loops with more than three major time constants are so difficult to stabilize satisfactorily that every effort should be made to reduce the number to three or to break the loop into two cascaded simpler loops. Major time constants are those resulting in break frequencies below or not far above the open-loop unity gain frequency. The original open-loop characteristic can have more than three major time constants, but all in excess of three will have to be substantially canceled by phase advance networks, as discussed in Chap. 11, to achieve acceptable closed-loop stability. In general, this process is difficult to do for more than two or three time constants, so it is undesirable to have too many in the original characteristic. In addition, there will always be quite a few minor time constants, meaning time constants that cause increases in the slope of the gain curve starting well above the unity gain frequency. The effect of a few minor time constants is usually negligible, but if too many are present, they have to be taken into account. The easiest way to handle multiple minor time constants is to treat them as transport lags, as we saw in Chap. 6.

Bode Plot Characterization of Third-Order Loops

A typical open-loop Bode plot with three major time constants appears in Fig. 10-1. In Chaps. 8 and 9 we saw that, for direct coupled

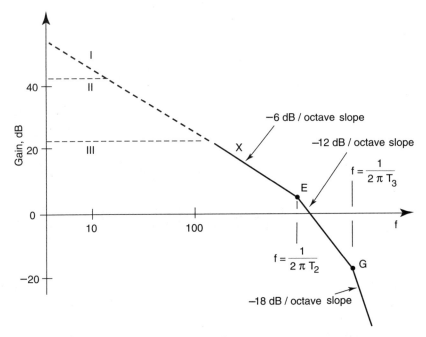

Figure 10-1. Bode plots for loops with three time constants.

loops, the details of the low-frequency characteristics, as depicted by dashed curves I, II, or III, have very little effect on closed-loop characteristics, including stability, so we will ignore the portion of the plot below X. The longest time constant will cause the slope of -6 dB/octave at X, the next longest will give the increase in slope to -12 dB/octave at point E, and the third and shortest will further increase the slope to -18 dB/octave at point G. What we would like is a family of curves serving the same purpose for third-order loops that the single curve of Fig. 9-4 serves for second-order loops. Each separate curve needs to be labeled with the difference in gain between breakpoints E and G. For very large values of the difference, the curves will closely approach the curve of Fig. 9-4, but for small values of difference the peaking will be greater for any given value of gain at point E. Such curves, with interpolation as required, will give the peaking for third-order minimum phase loops with open-loop characteristics shown in Fig. 10-1.

Computer Simulation of a Third-Order Loop

The general approach used to develop the curve in Fig. 9-4 could be used, but it would be much more difficult because of the third time constant. Also, a number of curves are needed, so the mathematical effort required would be considerable, even with the aid of a computer. As an alternative, since this book is not intended to be a math text, we will use a computer in a different and easier way, namely, as a loop simulator. The standard program for this application is SPICE, which is an acronym for Simulation Program, Integrated Circuit Emphasis. Originally developed about 1972 by Donald Pederson and his colleagues at the University of California at Berkeley, SPICE was put into the public domain and has been upgraded many times. Several commercial software vendors have also published versions of the program. At first it could be run only on mainframes, but versions for workstations and personal computers quickly became available as those tools became more powerful. It is probably safe to say that SPICE is the most highly developed and extensively used *computer-aided engineering* (CAE) program in history. In addition to electrical engineers, physicists, mechanical engineers, chemists, biologists, and others have used it when their problems could be represented by electrical analogs.

Engineers who rely excessively on computer simulation will have trouble developing enough understanding of what is going on to be able to exploit fully the great power of the computer. They will also be unable to cope with simple problems in the field where there is no access to CAE. At the other extreme, engineers who fail to use CAE to good advantage when appropriate handicap themselves unnecessarily. A good middle course is to use simple tools for simple problems and to resort to the computer for more difficult problems, as well as for help in developing the simple tools. The latter is what we are doing now, simulating the loop shown in Fig. 10-2, with several sets of parameter values. The results are plotted in Fig. 10-3. The curve farthest to the right in Fig. 10-3 is for a second-order system. It is the same as the curve in Fig. 9-4, but it is convenient to have it on this graph also. The lower scale is for use with this curve only.

Time domain characteristics for third-order loops were developed using SPICE simulations of the loop of Fig. 10-2 with a step function input. The presentation of results will be deferred until Chap. 12, however, in order to allow some preliminary discussion that relates to several chapters.

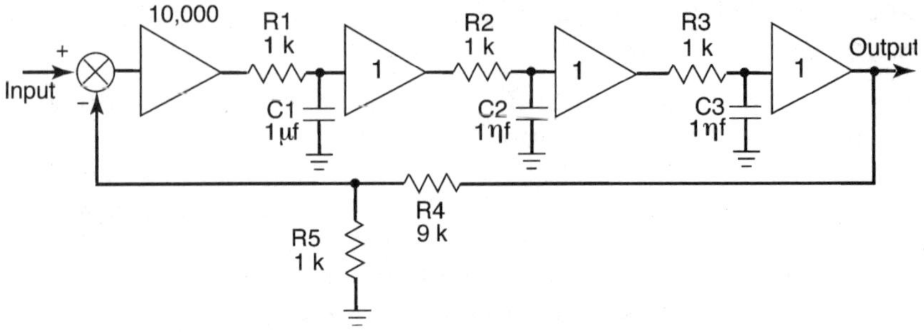

Figure 10-2. Schematic used for computer simulations of minimum phase loops with three time constants.

Utilization of Transfer Functions and Bode Plots

This is a convenient place to review our use of transfer functions and Bode plots. Frequency domain transfer functions have been used to determine frequency domain characteristics of several simple MPN loops. From the frequency domain characteristics, time domain characteristics can be obtained, theoretically, by inverse Fourier transformation, or practically, by equivalent methods. The equivalent methods are easier for only a few simple open-loop frequency domain characteristics that will not begin to cover the range of open-loop characteristics we encounter before undertaking compensation. Nevertheless, these few simple characteristics are adequate for almost all loops, since appropriate compensation will convert most original open-loop characteristics into one of the simple characteristics for which design curves have been developed. Once the curves are developed, there is no need to deal with transfer functions or Fourier transforms at all, since we can handle both compensation and application of the curves with Bode plots alone. Consequently, we have not needed to get involved with either complicated frequency domain transfer functions or time domain transfer functions.

Higher-Order Loops

It is unnecessary to continue along the present lines to models with four or more major time constants. To have reasonable closed-loop stability, any open-loop time constants in excess of three, after compensation is completed, must be so short that they will have the same effect as transport lags. All of these very short time constants can be added

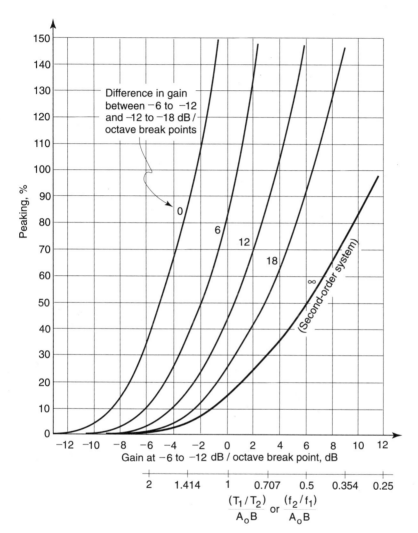

Figure 10-3. Peaking for minimum phase loops with three time constants as a function of open-loop Bode gain plot parameters. The lower scale is for only the right-hand curve.

up, and the resulting equivalent transport lag, if large enough to be troublesome, can be handled by the methods discussed in Chap. 16. The exact number and disposition of these time constants is irrelevant, since only the sum is of any consequence. In effect, the exact shape of the open-loop gain characteristic at very high frequencies is irrelevant, in the sense that different characteristics can cause the same amount of excess phase, which is all that matters. This topic is not important enough to warrant a detailed discussion here, but an interesting treatment, based on Eq. (5.1) with the range of integration changed, can be found in Thomason (1955, p. 185).

11

Loop Compensation

When the essential elements of a feedback loop are first connected, the resulting open-loop gain characteristic will usually be flat at low frequencies and then roll off with frequency at an ever increasing rate for a long ways, becoming too steep before the unity gain crossover frequency is reached to provide satisfactory closed-loop performance. The process of modifying the initial open-loop gain characteristic so that the closed-loop performance will be satisfactory is commonly referred to as *loop compensation,* or just *compensation.*

The Initial Characteristic

The process usually involves three main steps:

1. Determination of the initial open-loop characteristic.
2. Determination of the desired final open-loop gain characteristic.
3. Design of networks to convert the initial to the final characteristic.

The first step could be accomplished, theoretically, by opening the loop at any point, introducing a sinusoidal test signal headed in a forward direction around the loop, measuring the resulting amplitude and phase at the other end of the break, and repeating the measurement at a number of frequencies spaced through the range of interest, extending from low frequencies to well above the crossover frequency. If the loop can be assumed to be minimum phase to a reasonable approximation, the phase measurement can be omitted, which is a major simplification, since it is much more difficult than the gain measurement when made with simple instruments. While the assumption of minimum phase in any instance may seem dangerous, with due care it can be as reasonable as the assumption of linearity that we make implicitly every time we undertake a gain measurement at all.

Practically, this approach is usually difficult if not impossible because of two factors. When the gain extends down to zero frequency, as is usually the case, the entire loop must be direct coupled, which causes the bias conditions for every component to be established by feedback. When the feedback is eliminated by opening the loop, an artificial bias must be provided for the duration of the test. However, due to the high open-loop gain that is desirable for good closed-loop performance, elements well around the loop from the break are apt to be biased out of their linear region, rendering measurements impossible.

Accordingly, we must usually rely on data sheet information or on measurements on individual components or small groups of components. The results can be combined by simply adding the logarithmic gains and phase at each frequency to give the composite open-loop characteristic, which can be done most easily with the aid of Bode plots.

If any significant resonant peaks are evident, we should deal with them first (see Chap. 15). Then one final step is in order, converting the curve back to an asymptotic form to make the break frequencies more explicit. This step is easily accomplished with the aid of a cardboard template made up with slopes of -6, -12, and -18 dB/octave for the semilog graph paper and vertical scale used for plotting the open-loop gain. We position the template with one of the slopes tangent to the curve and extend a straight line in both directions through the point of tangency. We repeat this procedure for the other slopes; the low-frequency gain extends horizontally. The straight segments provide the asymptotic plot, and the intersections are the break frequencies.

The Final Characteristic

The second step is somewhat less straightforward. For the most part we will seek a curve with the shape of one of the curves that we analyzed in Chaps. 8 through 10. This curve must be positioned vertically to ensure satisfactory closed loop stability and as far to the right as possible to provide maximum bandwidth and rapid transient response. The desired curve will usually cross the initial open-loop gain curve at one or more points, meaning that gain will have to be added in certain regions, usually around and above the crossover frequency, and thrown away in others, normally well below the unity gain frequency. It is generally a good idea to fit the desired curve to the initial curve so that the amount of gain added and thrown away is moderate and so that less is added than is thrown away. These suggestions are rather conservative and usually result in fairly simple compensation with a little cushion for accommodating a small amount of unknown excess phase or other unforeseen harmful factors. If this advice seems a bit soft, it would be appropriate to mention that feedback loop design cannot be an exact science because we can seldom know in advance the exact nature of the input and disturbance signals we will encounter.

In relatively rare instances it may be necessary or desirable to have the slope steeper than -6 dB/octave well below the unity gain crossover frequency, but we will defer consideration of that condition until later in Chap. 17.

Step 2 involves using the results developed in Chaps. 9 and 10 in a reverse direction. That is, where closed-loop performance characteristics were determined from the open-loop gain curve, we now want to develop an open-loop gain curve that will result in closed-loop performance that meets given specifications. For second-order minimum phase systems, we can focus attention on the transition point between roll-off at -6 and -12 dB/octave. The vertical position of this point can be determined from the peaking specification with the aid of Fig. 10-3. Alternatively, if time domain performance is of more concern, the vertical position can be determined from an overshoot specification using Fig. 12-3, to be developed shortly. The horizontal position governs bandwidth in the frequency domain and rise time in the time domain. It can be determined from relations developed in Chaps. 9 and 12. Another possibility that is sometimes acceptable is to adjust the vertical position to meet the stability specification, and to let the bandwidth or rise time come out to whatever results from the components in the loop.

Modifying the Initial Characteristic

After steps 1 and 2 are complete, subtraction of the initial curve from the final curve gives a Bode plot of the gain modifications needed. They can usually be made with one or two phase retard networks and one or two phase advance networks. If undue difficulty is encountered, it is often desirable to go back and modify the final characteristics somewhat. The necessary modifications are fairly obvious when all the curves are right in front of you. In some cases we may also have to modify the original open-loop characteristic by changing some components if their characteristics are inadequate to meet the final closed-loop specifications, even with a reasonable amount of feedback.

Only a few options are available to effect the desired modifications. The simplest is to lower the entire open-loop gain curve. This approach is frequently used with laboratory temperature controllers that have a gain control knob on the front panel. Gain adjustment enables us to attain adequate stability under any of the varied conditions under which we use such controllers but only by throwing away to a greater or lesser degree the benefits of feedback. It is an example of adjusting the gain to achieve adequate stability, and accepting the resulting dynamic characteristics. We can obtain the same effect for type 1 loops by increasing the time constant of the integrator.

Another very simple approach is to increase the value of the longest time constant. This method is usually satisfactory only when that time constant is at the output and the purpose of the loop is to regulate the output to a constant value despite disturbances, for example, increasing the size of the capacitor at the output of a voltage regulator or adding a flywheel to machinery whose speed of rotation is to be held constant. This approach is sometimes referred to as *dominant lag stabilization,* since one lag provides all the roll-off needed to achieve adequate stability.

Figure 11-1 shows the next step up in sophistication. Here a phase retard network has been added to start the roll-off at a lower frequency, but without affecting the very low frequency gain. The gain at the -6 to -12 dB/octave breakpoint is reduced by the attenuation of the phase retard network.

Another possibility, illustrated in Fig. 11-2, is to leave the first break frequency intact and use a phase advance network to increase the second break frequency. The original low-frequency and midband gain are retained, while still lowering the gain at the -6 to -12 dB/octave breakpoint. In Figs. 11-2 and 11-8, it is assumed that the phase advance is provided by a capacitor in the feedback network, as discussed in the next paragraph. Then the low-frequency attenuation of the phase advance is taken account of in the value of B.

The most common place for a phase advance network is in the B path of a loop, as shown in Fig. 11-3. This placement not only results in extreme simplicity, only a single capacitor being required, but also provides another benefit. It eliminates a high-frequency lag resulting from the equivalent resistance of the feedback network and the input capacitance of the op amp, shown dashed. With the phase advance capacitor in place, the only effect of the input capacitance is to change the effec-

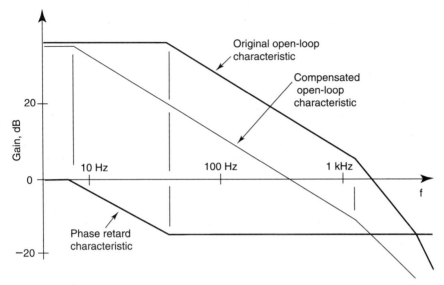

Figure 11-1. Use of a phase retard network to modify the original open-loop characteristic.

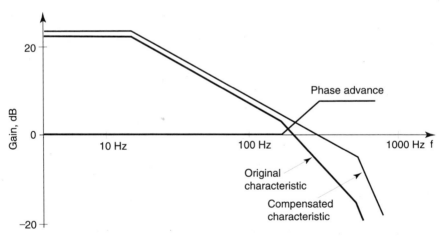

Figure 11-2. Use of a phase advance network to modify the original open-loop characteristic.

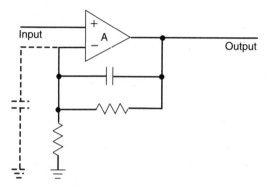

Figure 11-3. Common method of implement-
ing phase advance in the feedback path.

tive value of the phase advance capacitor very slightly. When this step
is taken, the input capacitance is said to have been *assimilated.*

Location of Phase Advance Characteristics

Phase advance in the feedback path invalidates the assumption we
have made so far that B is a constant, independent of frequency.
However, if the phase advance in the B path is around the crossover
frequency, it will have very little effect on closed-loop characteristics,
other than its effect on loop stability. By the time it might cause roll-off
through the factor $1/B$, the closed-loop gain is determined mainly by
the forward gain, as discussed in Chap. 8. Therefore, the decrease in
$1/B$ has little effect, except possibly to lower slightly the break frequency or to steepen slightly the slope of the closed-loop roll-off. Bode
plots for this situation appear in Fig. 11-4. Phase advance at frequencies well below the crossover frequency, if desirable, must be in the A
path if the goal is flat closed-loop gain.

Phase Advance in a Typical Application

With the simple circuit of Fig. 11-3, the frequency range of the phase
advance is $1/B$. If this range is excessive, it can be cut back to any
desired value by adding a small resistor in series with the phase
advance capacitor. If, on the other hand, the range is insufficient, more
gain will have to be added. The best place for this extra gain is usually

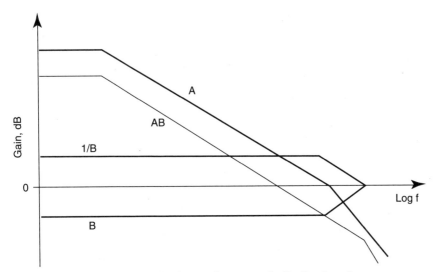

Figure 11-4. Bode plots with phase advance in the feedback path.

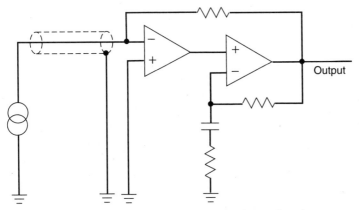

Figure 11-5. Use of phase advance in the forward path to compensate a lag caused by the feedback resistor and source capacitance.

in the A path, as just mentioned. Figure 11-5 shows this solution for a current-to-voltage conversion circuit. The symbol at the left, two overlapping circles, is for a current source, which might be a photodiode or an ionization gauge, for example. Because of the high source impedance, nominally infinite, the source must be hooked up with a shielded cable to avoid excessive noise pickup, and the cable will have significant capacitance. This capacitance, plus the source capacitance and amplifier input capacitance, together with the feedback resistor, introduces another lag into the loop, and it may have quite a long time constant if the feedback resistor is very large. The product of the resistor value and the current to be measured should result in a voltage substantially larger than any amplifier offset, or drift voltage, or any thermoelectric potentials. Some sources require feedback resistors on the order of 10^9, or perhaps 10^{10} Ω. Higher values are usually undesirable because their stability is subject to degradation by surface leakage due to humidity and contamination.

If such a high value is needed for the feedback resistor, using capacitance around it is a tricky business, although it has been done. Ordinary capacitors cannot be used because of excessive leakage, but wires from the ends of the feedback resistor can be bent into proximity, the configuration being referred to as a "gimmick." An alternative approach appears in Fig. 11-5, where the second op amp has been connected to give a large amount of phase advance to effectively cancel the roll-off of the feedback lag up to beyond the crossover frequency. The local feedback around the second op amp alone is a phase retard network, resulting in closed-loop gain with a phase advance characteristic, since the closed-loop gain is the reciprocal of the feedback gain. Ultimately, of course, the closed-loop gain of the phase advance circuit will roll off the same as the op amp open-loop gain characteristic, introducing a few more lags into the main loop. With modern video op amps, however, the time constants of these lags can be so short that the resulting equivalent transport lag is negligible.

The feedback maintains the center conductor of the coaxial cable at a virtual ground, as discussed in Chap. 13, so that the source does not have to charge the cable capacitance, which would be extremely slow, and leakage is minimized. Nevertheless, the cable capacitance is by no means irrelevant and should be kept as low as possible. At high frequencies it shorts out the feedback so that the equivalent input noise voltage of the first amplifier appears at the output multiplied by the A path gain, rather than by the closed-loop gain, resulting in excessive high-frequency noise. The greater the cable capacitance, the lower the frequency at which this trouble sets in, and it is aggravated in this example by the great increase in high-frequency forward gain contributed by the phase advance in the A path.

Even when the input capacitance is assimilated, this problem is usually present to some degree, although not as obviously. This problem is one reason to avoid, if possible, much phase advance below the crossover frequency, where the phase advance must be in the forward path. In addition, if the roll-off provided by the longer time constants is postponed, in effect, by large amounts of phase advance, then the shorter time constants will have a more important role around the unity gain frequency. The shorter time constants are apt to result from parasitic reactances and other factors that tend to be unknown, uncontrollable, unstable, or subject to wide variation between different units. Consequently, it is usually better to get the open-loop gain below unity before this potential quagmire is reached.

This tactic suggests a simple and conservative approach to compensation for many simple loops when the closed loop gain is five to ten, or more. First, a capacitor is added to the feedback network, as shown in Fig. 11-3, to assimilate the input capacitance and raise the frequency at which the slope of the open-loop gain characteristic is increased by the second longest time constant. The capacitor value is chosen to start the phase advance at the break frequency caused by the second longest time constant, as shown in Fig. 11-2. For the reason just mentioned, it is well to limit this phase advance to a moderate amount, for example, 20 dB, by means of a small resistor in series with the capacitor if the closed loop gain is much more than 20 dB. Then, the gain at that frequency is lowered to provide the desired stability, using a phase retard network in the forward path below the original first-break frequency, as shown in Fig. 11-4. For a type 1 loop, the adjustment is made by increasing the time constant of the integrator. After this adjustment, the phase advance will be mostly or entirely above the unity gain frequency, where it normally belongs.

Frequently two phase retard networks will be employed, in which case the one with the longer time constant should be placed either right after the summing junction or as close to it as possible. The error signal is smaller there than after some amplification, which minimizes the adverse effect of the phase retard network on slew rate capability.

Final Characteristic with Steeper Slope below the Unity Gain Frequency

Now let us return to characteristics with a slope steeper than -6 dB/octave well below the unity gain frequency. For maximum closed-loop bandwidth and fastest rise time, you want the open-loop gain to be as high as possible up to the highest possible frequency. Thus it seems regrettable that in most instances you have to throw away some high-frequency gain with a phase retard network in order to achieve the characteristics we have been discussing so far. One way to improve the situation is to start the roll-off at a higher frequency and to use a steeper slope initially. This slope should be reduced to approximately

−20 dB/decade somewhat before the unity gain crossover frequency is reached and held there until somewhat above the crossover frequency. Because of the shape of Bode's weighting function, the phase at the crossover frequency is determined mainly by the −20 dB/decade segment, so that the phase will only moderately exceed −90° there. This approach provides good stability, even though the phase will be much higher at lower frequencies. In fact, the phase can exceed 180° without resulting in oscillation, provided it is back down before the unity gain frequency is reached.

However, a word of caution is in order. Anything that lowers the entire open-loop gain characteristic momentarily, such as a power supply glitch or an overload condition, can drop the crossover point down to where the phase is higher. If in the course of this excursion a phase of exactly 180° is encountered, oscillation will start. Theoretically the oscillation would build up in amplitude exponentially forever, but practically it will quickly be limited by nonlinearities that have the effect of reducing the average gain throughout a cycle to just the value, unity, needed to sustain the oscillation at that amplitude. As a result, the oscillation may continue even after conditions have returned to normal. Consequently, loops of this type are frequently referred to as "conditionally stable." Obviously, it is desirable to avoid this state because of the potential for sustained oscillation.

If performance requirements demand it, an easy way to achieve a −40 dB/decade initial slope is to cascade two identical op amps that are both internally compensated with a slope of −20 dB/decade up to approximately the crossover frequency. Using both sections of a dual op amp is convenient, but better overall characteristics can be achieved by picking the first op amp for superior input noise, input impedance, and drift specifications, while picking the second for power output and slew rate capability. The initial break frequency for both should be the same, however, to keep the steepest part of the slope as far below the unity gain crossover frequency as possible. The composite open-loop gain characteristic of the op amp tandem appears in Fig. 11-6. If the closed-loop gain of the complete loop is quite high, corresponding to open-loop gain substantially less than that of the pair of op amps, the easiest way to reduce the slope through the crossover frequency is to use one or perhaps two phase advance networks.

To avoid the risk of conditional stability, it is well to avoid approaching a phase shift of 180° too closely below the crossover frequency. About −135°, corresponding to a slope of about −9 dB/octave, is a reasonable compromise. No network has that slope, but it can be approximated with alternate asymptotic slopes of −6 and −12 dB/octave in fairly close proximity, or for the sake of simplicity, with a single seg-

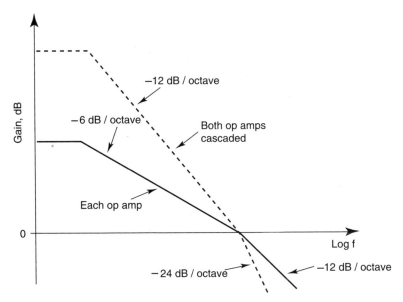

Figure 11-6. Bode plot of two identical op amps cascaded.

ment at -12 dB/octave sandwiched between segments of 0 or -6 dB/octave slopes. The frequency span of the -12 dB/octave segment needs to be restricted so that the maximum phase does not exceed about $-135°$. In this situation it may be well to round off the asymptotic gain curve to get a good picture of the situation, as in Fig. 4-7.

Another way to steepen the slope initially is to use a phase retard network that cuts in at the same frequency as the first break in the original open-loop characteristic, as illustrated in Fig. 11-7.

Two phase retard networks starting at the same frequency, but lower than the first break frequency of the initial characteristic, could be used if it is necessary to start the attenuation at a lower frequency than the first break frequency of the initial characteristic. One of the phase retard networks should drop out at the initial first break frequency, and the other should drop out somewhat below the unity gain frequency. Around the unity gain crossover frequency, it may be necessary to use a phase advance network if another lag is steepening the slope at that point. Some cases may require two phase advance networks. Usually a capacitor in the B path will suffice for one phase advance, but if a second is needed, another op amp hooked up like the second one in Fig. 11-5 will be needed. Bode plots for this arrangement appear in Fig. 11-8. The salient features are a segment with a slope of -6 dB/octave approximately centered on the unity gain frequency,

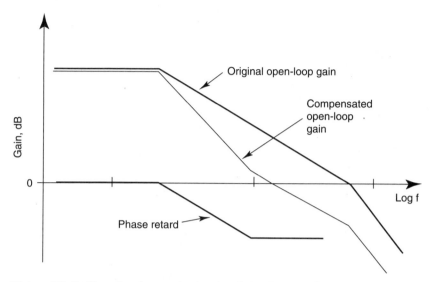

Figure 11-7. Use of a phase retard network to obtain a slope steeper than −6 dB/octave below the unity gain frequency.

with steeper slope above and below. For a type 1 loop, the curve is identical except for replacement of the horizontal segment with a segment having a slope of −6 dB/octave extending down to zero frequency.

In Fig. 11-9 we have duplicated the final compensated open-loop gain curve of Fig. 11-8 and added a curve without the steeper low-frequency slope, but with similar gain around the crossover point, thus giving similar stability. The shaded area represents the midband open-loop gain that is picked up by using the steeper slope. The most noticeable beneficial effect on closed-loop performance is improved rise time that is approximately proportional to the improvement in the open-loop rise time. That value will be about $1/\sqrt{2}$ times the ratio of the first break frequency of the steeper curve to the first break frequency of the other. With two equal time constants for the steeper curve, the combined rise time will be about $\sqrt{2}$ times the rise time of each. The other improvement in performance is a stiffer output at high frequencies. This enhancement is usually much less noticeable, but may be important in some instances.

The price for these benefits includes not only increased complexity but also some impairment of stability.

Any effort to improve stability by using a slope less than −6 dB/octave through the unity gain frequency, where Bode's weighting

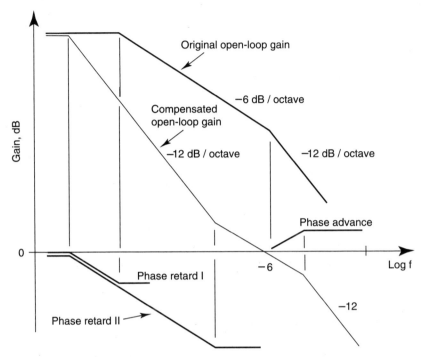

Figure 11-8. More complex compensation yielding a steeper slope below the unity gain frequency.

function is greatest, would be questionable. Only a slight change in gain could shift the crossover frequency to a region of much greater slope.

For most ordinary requirements, the steeper characteristic is probably not worth the additional effort and the likelihood of increased overshoot. However, for those readers who are interested, a thorough discussion of many aspects of the subject can be found in Graeme (1989).

Placement and Implementation of Phase Retard Networks

Before leaving the subject of compensation, we should say a little more about where to incorporate phase retard characteristics. For open-loop gain, the location in the loop is irrelevant. However, since the attenua-

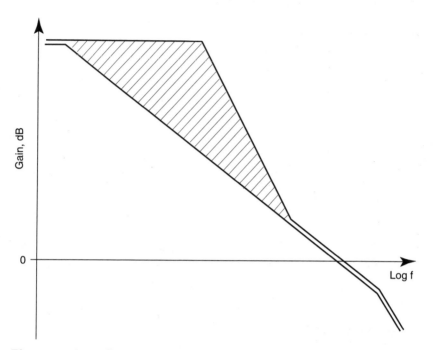

Figure 11-9. Midband gain picked up by using a steeper slope below the unity gain frequency.

tion is usually desired well below the unity gain frequency, phase retard networks should usually be confined to the A path so as not to impair the flatness of the low-frequency closed-loop gain through the factor $1/B$. An exception occurs if something other than a flat closed-loop characteristic is desired, as in the local feedback loop of Fig. 11-5.

In the old days, it was customary to parallel vacuum tube or transistor load resistors in the A path with a series combination of a capacitor and a resistor. This technique gave a heuristic sense of improving stability by adding the electrical equivalent of a shock absorber. Now that gain is usually provided by op amps, which preclude access to such points, phase retard characteristics can be implemented by simply incorporating a phase retard circuit, as shown in Fig. 4-4, in the forward path, with buffering if necessary. Alternatively, the gain of an op amp providing gain in the A path can be shaped by using phase advance in a local feedback path around the op amp, as shown in Fig. 11-3.

These comments, as well as earlier comments about placement of phase advance networks, apply to direct coupled loops. For the rare loops with two or more blocking capacitors or transformers, low-frequency stability becomes a problem also, and phase at the lower unity gain frequency must be controlled. In this region phase advance and phase retard swap roles, which applies to all the comments about placement as well.

12
Time Domain Characteristics

Relationship between Time Domain and Frequency Domain Characteristics

We return now to the time domain characteristics of the two- and three-time-constant minimum phase loops whose frequency domain characteristics were covered in Chaps. 9 and 10, respectively. To begin, we recall that we can easily obtain both the frequency and time domain characteristics of single-time-constant loops covered in Chap. 8 from the closed-loop frequency domain transfer function. For two- and three-time-constant loops, ascertaining closed-loop time domain characteristics from the closed-loop frequency domain transfer function is much less easy, which is why we deferred the matter, but it is still possible in principle. The important point is that although both frequency and time domain parameters are determined by the frequency domain transfer function, it is equally valid to say that any one of the three determines the other two. Thus, in principle, after the frequency domain characteristics have been determined, we can use them to obtain the time domain characteristics. We can do so without going through the transfer function, although that approach is also possible.

The mathematical basis for this calculation is the Fourier transform. The Fourier transform of the delta function response of a system gives the amplitude and phase characteristics, just as if they had been measured with a sine wave input swept slowly through the frequency range of interest (Weaver, 1983, p. 156). This result follows from the fact that the Fourier transform of a delta function has constant amplitude and zero phase at all frequencies, the same as a swept sine wave test signal (Weaver, 1983, p. 77).

A delta function is zero at all times except one instant, at which time it becomes very large, nominally infinite, but so that the time integral has a finite value. Thus its integral is a step function, and the derivative of a step function is a delta function.

To go the other way, as we want to do now, start with the amplitude and phase characteristics, determined experimentally, analytically, or however, and perform an inverse Fourier transform. The result is the time domain output that would occur with a delta function stimulus. What we normally want, however, is the step function response, which can be obtained by integrating the delta function response. Because this technique may not be intuitively obvious, consider a system A with a transfer function of unity, followed by an integrator, as shown in Fig. 12-1. Clearly the delta function response of system A is a delta function, and the integral of a delta function is obviously a step function, since the integral is constant at all times except for a jump or step at the time when the delta function occurs. With a transfer function of unity, the output of system A in response to a step function input is a step function, so the integral of the delta function response is identical to the step function response. Because of linearity, this relationship will hold for any transfer function of system A.

We have focused on the amplitude characteristic, or spectrum, in the frequency domain, which by itself does not suffice to allow the inverse Fourier transform to be calculated. However, the phase, which is also needed, could be calculated from the transfer function. Alternatively, for minimum phase systems, the phase characteristic can be deter-

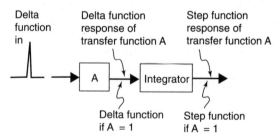

Figure 12-1. Relationship between delta function response and step function response.

mined from the amplitude characteristic with the aid of Bode's integral formula, Eq. (5.1). Then the step function response of the system can be determined from the frequency domain amplitude response spectrum using the signal processing shown in Fig. 12-2. All the steps could be combined into a single new transform pair, which for minimum phase systems would take you directly from the complete amplitude response function in the frequency domain to the step function response in the time domain, or vice versa. Apparently such a transform pair has not yet been developed, but that is not too important, since we would find it cumbersome to use even with the aid of a computer. Compounding the difficulty is the fact that the exact gain curve from zero to infinite frequency is needed as the input, while we have determined only the main features of interest with our simplified approach. The important point is that the method is feasible theoretically, which means that various equivalent approaches are also possible. What we would really like for a final result is something much simpler, namely, curves giving the overshoot as a function of gain at the different breakpoints. One way of determining points on such curves would be to inverse transform and integrate several gain curves with different values of gain at the break frequency and then plot the overshoot of the resulting time domain responses against the gain values.

Computer Simulation to Obtain Time Domain Characteristics

Since considerable effort with a computer would be involved, a reasonable alternative is to resort to SPICE simulations again. The loop of Fig. 10-2, with a step function input, gives the step function response

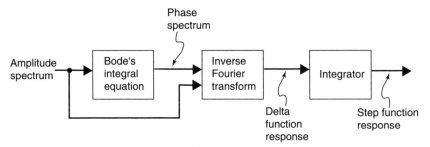

Figure 12-2. Signal processing to determine step function response from amplitude spectrum.

from which the overshoot can be read off directly. The lag circuit time
constants and the low-frequency open-loop gain, provided by the
amplifiers that also provide buffering to prevent loading effects, are
adjusted to give the several values of gain at the breakpoint. The
results are plotted in Fig. 12-3, which gives overshoot in the same way
that Fig. 10-3 gives peaking. Reference to Figs. 8-3 and 10-1 will recall
the significance of the parameters.

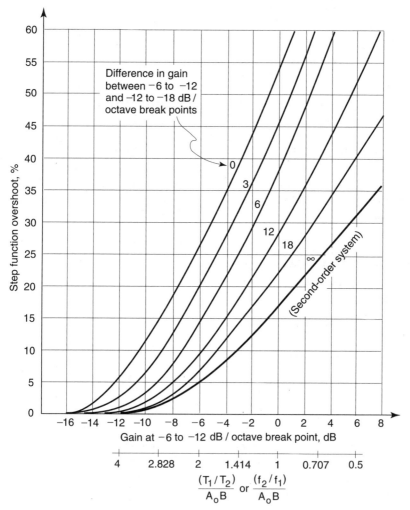

Figure 12-3. Step function overshoot for minimum phase loops with three
time constants as a function of open-loop Bode gain plot parameters. Lower
scale is for only the right-hand curve.

As in previous graphs of this type, two x-axis scales are provided. The upper scale is used if the open-loop gain information is in the form of a Bode plot, for type 1 loops, and for third-order systems. The lower scale provides the ultimate in convenience for type 0 second-order systems when loop information is in the form of time constants or break frequencies, and the low-frequency gain. This scale applies only to the curve farthest to the right, which is for second-order systems.

Alternative Representations of Stability

For second-order minimum phase systems, performance characteristics can also be plotted against several other parameters that are themselves functions of the open-loop time constants and low-frequency gain. The principal parameters used in traditional feedback literature are the damping factor ζ and the phase margin, while logarithmic decrement is another that is less widely used. Damping factor is defined only for second-order minimum phase systems and is of little intrinsic interest. However, since it is prominent in the literature, a graphical relationship to the two parameters used in our development appears in Fig. 12-4. Also in this figure is phase margin, which is the difference between the open-loop phase and 180° at the unity gain frequency. Like damping factor, phase margin is an internal parameter of limited final interest, but at least it exists for any type of system, of course. When excess phase is present, phase margin becomes a much more important design parameter, as we will see in Chap. 16. An interesting feature of Fig. 12-4 is that over most of the range of interest, phase margin and damping factor are quite similar, except for a factor of 100 when the phase margin is in degrees.

Obviously, several other curves could be developed to provide correlation among the five parameters that have been mentioned, namely, $(T_1/T_2)/A_oB$, open-loop gain at the -6 dB/octave to -12 dB/octave transition point, damping factor, phase margin, and logarithmic decrement. However, most of the curves can be done without quite well, so we will stop with Fig. 12-4. The important thing is to realize that all five parameters express the same information in different ways and that the two parameters used for the x-axis scales of Figs. 10-3 and 12-3 are the easiest to use and most direct for feedback loop design and analysis.

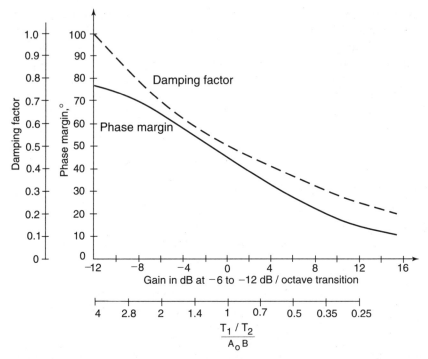

Figure 12-4. Damping factor and phase margin for minimum phase loops with two time constants as a function of open-loop Bode gain plot parameters.

Conditions for Zero Peaking and Overshoot

It is interesting, and perhaps a bit surprising, that the requirement for no peaking in the frequency domain is not quite the same as the requirement for no overshoot to a step function in the time domain. The ratio of time constants must be two times the low frequency gain to prevent peaking completely but four times to prevent overshoot completely. These limiting cases have been around for a long time as rules of thumb (Thomason, 1955, pp. 126 and 251, for example). It is unfortunate that zero overshoot is harder to achieve, since it is necessary occasionally, while the need for zero peaking is extremely rare. However, the peaking goes up faster than the overshoot as the gain at the −6 to −12 dB/octave slope transition increases. Consequently, the curves cross over at about 18 percent overshoot and peaking, when the gain at the transition point is about ½ dB above zero.

Rise Time

The other time domain characteristic of particular interest is the rise time. We can obtain this parameter directly from SPICE simulations, just as we obtained overshoot. However, for most purposes we can easily estimate rise time with adequate accuracy. First, we recall from Chap. 8 that the closed-loop rise time for a single-time-constant loop is the open-loop rise time divided by the low-frequency open-loop gain. To a large degree this calculation will hold for practical two- or three-time-constant loops as well. For them the open-loop rise time will be governed mainly by the longest time constant. The other time constant or constants must be much shorter to provide good stability, and the rise times of cascaded lags combine approximately as the square root of the sum of the squares (Valley and Wallman, 1948, p. 77), making the much shorter ones irrelevant as far as overall open-loop rise time is concerned. When the ratio of time constants is sufficient to eliminate overshoot completely, the rise time estimated on this basis will be quite accurate, and will be about twice the longest time constant, divided by the low-frequency loop gain. When there is some overshoot, the rise time will be reduced, although not drastically, even though the open-loop rise time is slightly increased by the additional time constant causing the overshoot. The decrease in closed-loop rise time results from the phase shift that is making the feedback go from negative to positive at high frequencies, thus augmenting the high-frequency closed-loop gain. The result is that for moderate overshoot, the rise time drops to approximately 1.4 times the longest time constant divided by the low-frequency loop gain. As stability deteriorates further, the rise time goes back up unless a transport lag causes the deterioration. In the rare cases when a more accurate determination of rise time is needed, Fig. 12-5 will be helpful. This figure shows the dependence of rise time on loop stability, with the latter represented by step function overshoot, along the x axis. The figure is based on a number of simulations of second- and third-order minimum phase loops.

The preceding discussion applies to loops with two or more lags, but no integrator, so that the zero-frequency gain is finite. When an integrator is present, its time constant can be consolidated with any other open-loop gain factors and then divided by B to give the closed-loop time constant, just as was done at the end of Chap. 8. The rise time will be about 1.4 to 2 times this value, depending on the overshoot, as just discussed. An alternative approach is to invert the closed-loop asymptotic break angular frequency to get the longest closed-loop time constant and then multiply by the appropriate value in the 1.4 to 2.2 range. This alternative may have less potential for con-

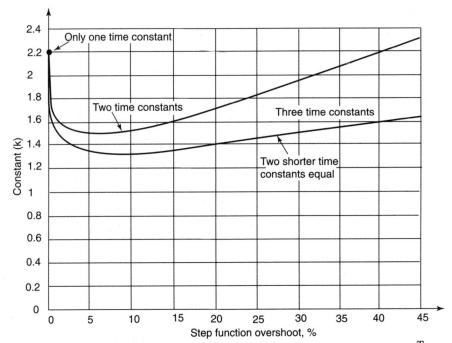

Figure 12-5. Dependence of rise time on step function overshoot. $T_r \approx k \dfrac{T_L}{A_O B}$. T_L = longest open-loop time constant.

fusion, especially when working from Bode plots or when the integrator time constant has not been consolidated with other gain factors.

With two or more major time constants in the A path, the shape of the step function response changes from the simple shape shown in Fig. 8-4 for a loop with one time constant to something more like that shown in Fig. 8-3, which was used to define rise time. The change at the beginning of the rise is due to the filtering action of the second lag on the output of the first, which will have the shape shown in Fig. 8-4. The feedback causing the overshoot, and perhaps ringing, is responsible for the change in shape as the final value is approached.

The Trade-Off between Rise Time and Overshoot

We conclude this chapter by reflecting on just how rigid a control of step function overshoot we want, now that we are in a position to control it. We have two main factors to consider. One is the realism of a step function compared to the signals that will be experienced in actual operation. This topic was mentioned in Chap. 8 and is considered further in Chap. 16. The other factor is the seriousness of momentary errors resulting from overshoot or, on the other hand, from sluggish response due to measures to limit overshoot. Clearly there is a trade-off here, and we need some means of quantitating the error to facilitate determination of an optimum compromise. One possibility is to take the average of the absolute value of the error. In many cases, however, large errors are much more serious than small errors and should be weighted more heavily. An easy and reasonable approach is to square the error before averaging; the result is called the *mean square error*. This value is frequently, though by no means always, one of the better criteria for evaluating performance.

When we use the mean square error to evaluate the step function response of second-order minimum phase systems with monotonically increasing slope, we obtain optimum performance when the overshoot is about 10 percent. This condition occurs with a gain of −3 dB at the −6 to −12 dB/octave slope transition, which corresponds to a damping factor of 0.6 and a phase margin of 55°. Except for certain extremely stringent requirements, such as those on vertical deflection amplifiers for oscilloscopes or preamplifiers in data acquisition systems, this objective is often reasonable. The overshoots in operation will be substantially less than 10 percent for the most part because the inputs and disturbances do not change as fast as a step function does.

A more rigorous treatment of this matter involves a lot of advanced mathematics and is useful only if we have fairly accurate statistical characterization of the input and disturbances to be encountered. The experimental determination of such information is easier than it used to be, thanks to computerized data acquisition and processing. However, in most instances, this procedure still requires much more effort than is needed to do a little fine-tuning of the compensation after the system is in operation and its performance has been evaluated.

It should also be noted that zero overshoot, although necessary occasionally, is hard to achieve and costly in terms of rise time. Figure 12-5 shows that for a typical third-order system, about in the middle of the region labeled *Three time constants,* accepting about 3 percent overshoot to a step function will allow the rise time to be about 15 percent less than if no overshoot is allowed.

13
Operational Amplifiers

Although slightly deviating from the main thrust of this book, a chapter on operational amplifiers is not totally inappropriate, considering that these amplifiers provide the forward gain for most feedback loops. In addition, a brief discussion which touches on several important matters regarding loop stabilization may be of considerable historical interest for young engineers. For the author and other old-timers, this chapter is a sentimental journey recalling some of the exciting advances that we experienced in real time during our careers in engineering.

The concept of the operational amplifier was developed during World War II, with much of the early work being done by George A. Philbrick. The most important features of the concept are a differential input with good common mode rejection, direct coupling so as to provide response down to zero frequency, high voltage gain, and a single-ended output that is zero relative to ground with zero differential input voltage. Other desirable features include high-input impedance, low-input offset voltage, low-input offset drift with time and temperature, high bandwidth, internal compensation, small size, low power consumption, and low cost. Infinite gain is sometimes cited as ideal, but since it would make stabilization of any loop the op amp was used in impossible, we will settle for very high gain.

Vacuum Tube Op Amps

Early usage was largely in analog computers where the amplifiers were connected to perform mathematical operations such as addition, subtraction, and integration. This usage led to the name operational amplifier, soon shortened to op amp. After the war Philbrick and others produced commercial versions using miniature twin triodes, since transistors had not yet been invented. The two tubes, along with other components, were mounted in a base that plugged into a standard octal tube socket, making the unit modular. Typically the two sections of one tube were connected in a long-tailed pair configuration to provide a differential input, while the sections of the other tube provided additional gain. The biggest problem was level shifting to get the output back down to zero despite the large bias offset voltage between the grid and plate of a vacuum tube. The drop across a small neon lamp, on the order of 60 V, was sometimes exploited for this purpose, while in other cases resistive dividers were used. However, the latter called for quite high voltage supplies and considerable loss of gain.

In order that substantial feedback could be used without creating instability, the gain was usually rolled off at about 6 dB/octave up to the unity gain frequency, using a phase retard network for each triode. The longest time constant was placed at the first stage where the signal was smallest so as to minimize the adverse effect on slew rate capability. An overall low-frequency gain of about 3000 was regarded as good.

Transistor Op Amps

During the late 1950s transistors became suitable for op amps, resulting in several major improvements. Supply voltages could be greatly reduced, with plus and minus 15 V emerging as a standard. Power consumption and size were also greatly reduced, but the greatest benefit was simplification in handling the dc offset problem. By using PNP and NPN transistors in alternate stages, the bias offsets could be made to cancel out. Typically the units were built on printed circuit boards with an edge connector to provide modularity. Three or four common emitter stages were usually cascaded to provide sufficient voltage gain, and often an emitter follower or complementary emitter follower output stage provided low output impedance and high output current capability. For the differential input pair, a current source replaced the large resistor to a large supply voltage, resulting in improved common mode rejection ratio and a common mode voltage range not much less than the supply voltage range. Compensation was still handled primarily with a phase retard network for each gain stage. The only negative aspect of transistorization was lower input impedance than the vacuum tube op amps, but that problem was not too serious.

Monolithic Op Amps

The next big step forward occurred in the mid-1960s when monolithic integrated circuit technology had advanced far enough to accommodate analog circuitry. The first monolithic op amp to be widely used, the 709, was somewhat similar to discrete transistor op amps. The biggest improvements were in size and input offset drift specifications. The latter improvement resulted from the extremely close spacing of the two input differential pair transistors, minimizing the effect of thermal gradients, and from the fact that the transistors were produced simultaneously under virtually identical conditions.

Both PNP and NPN transistors had to be used to cancel dc offsets, but it was difficult to obtain good PNP characteristics with the monolithic processes of the time. This situation led to various ingenious schemes for combining a mediocre PNP with a good NPN so as to simulate a good PNP. The biggest problem, however, was with compensation; monolithic capacitors of moderate values required considerable die area, and large area per circuit reduced yield drastically as a result of the statistical impact of wafer defects. This problem was so intractable that internal compensation was omitted from the 709, making it useful by itself only as a comparator. Terminals were provided for connecting external compensation networks, but the need to design the networks and implement them during manufacture limited the acceptance of the 709.

The design of the LM101 by Bob Widlar in 1967 addressed this problem. Compensation required only a single 30-pF external capacitor. This capacitor was moved on chip in the 741, which followed shortly, and was otherwise similar, resulting in the first monolithic internally compensated op amp. It was a huge success immediately, being second sourced by most semiconductor manufacturers, and becoming a de facto industry standard. The key advance was reduction in the number of common emitter gain stages to only two, reducing the number of major time constants to two also. Of course, the gain of the two stages had to be increased substantially to provide adequate overall gain. The gain was achieved by using current source loads and an emitter-follower buffer after each common emitter stage.

In a simple common emitter stage, the voltage gain is approximately the transconductance times the load resistance, neglecting the effect of loading by the next stage. The transconductance varies linearly with the collector current; therefore any attempt to increase voltage gain by increasing the load resistance is completely offset by the concomitant decrease in transconductance due to decreased collector current, assuming that the bias voltage across the load resistor is kept the same. The result is that, for bipolar transistors in the common emitter configuration, the voltage gain is fixed at approximately 40 times the dc bias voltage across the load resistor for any resistor value or transistor. However, if a current source is substituted for the load resistor, the source can provide ample current to develop high transconductance in the transistor while still appearing as a high load impedance, resulting in very high voltage gain. The gain with a perfect current source would, in fact, be infinite in terms of the simple model used above, but at very high gains other factors that can be neglected at lower gains come in to impose a limit. Foremost among these factors is loading by the next stage, which can be minimized with an emitter-follower buffer, allowing stage gains approaching 1000, for op amp gains approaching 1,000,000 with only two gain stages. The emitter followers, by virtue of their very high cutoff frequency, do not cause nearly as much trouble for loop stabilization as do additional common emitter stages.

The lesson here relative to the main theme of this book is that the number of major time constants in any feedback loop should be held to an absolute minimum, preferably not more than two or three, to facilitate easy and satisfactory loop stabilization. Large loops with more major time constants should, if at all possible, be broken down into two cascaded loops.

Transistorized Current Sources

The current sources are implemented with an ingenious circuit known as a *current mirror*, a simple version being shown in Fig. 13-1. The current through the resistor will increase the base-to-emitter voltage of Q1 just enough to cause Q1's collector to carry the current, less the minute fraction needed as base current for Q1 and Q2. The same voltage applied to the base of Q2 will cause its collector to carry almost exactly the same current as that supplied by the resistor to Q1, irrespective of the collector voltage at Q2, due to the inherent characteristics of bipolar transistors. Thus the collector of Q2 looks like a current source. The equality of currents depends on the two transistors being virtually identical and at the same temperature, conditions that can be realized adequately only with monolithic fabrication. More transistor bases can

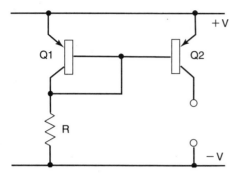

Figure 13-1. Rudimentary form of current mirror.

be connected to $Q1$ to provide multiple current sources, and by adjusting the area of those transistors relative to the area of $Q1$, proportional currents can be obtained. Furthermore, one of the currents can be run down to an NPN current mirror at the negative supply rail to provide one or more current sources of the opposite polarity. These could properly be called *current sinks*, although *current source* is the usual nomenclature for this circuit regardless of polarity. Thus a single resistor and several current mirrors can provide all the bias currents needed for an entire op amp.

A Basic Monolithic Bipolar Op Amp

A simplified schematic exemplifying many of the features of the 741 and similar op amps appears in Fig. 13-2. Transistors $Q1$ and $Q2$, the differential input pair, are the first common emitter gain stage. $Q3$ and $Q4$ constitute a current mirror reflecting the signal current from $Q1$ so that it is added to that of $Q2$, rather than being wasted. $Q4$ also serves as a current source load for $Q2$ so that the gain of the first stage is high. $Q5$ is a current source furnishing the operating current of the differential pair, thus providing good common mode rejection and a wide common mode voltage range. $Q6$ is the emitter follower buffer between the two common emitter gain stages, with $Q7$ being the second common emitter stage. $Q8$ is its current source load, while $Q9$ and $Q10$ are a complementary emitter follower output stage, buffering $Q7$ from the load. $Q11$ establishes the base voltage for current sources $Q5$ and $Q8$. The diode reduces crossover distortion in the output complementary emitter follower, but does not completely eliminate it, which would increase the risk of thermal runaway. The residual amount of

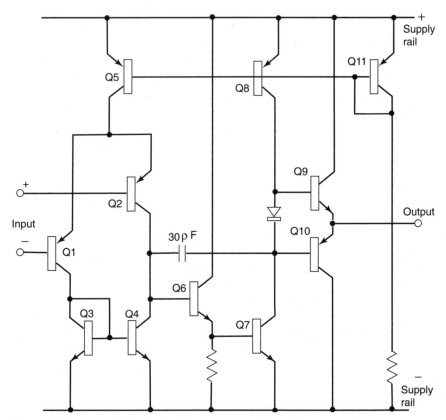

Figure 13-2. Simplified schematic of op amp with only two gain stages.

crossover distortion will normally be reduced to negligible proportions by feedback.

Although it is not apparent from this simplified schematic, with some refinement the PNP input pair can result in a common mode range extending slightly below the lower supply rail, since bipolar transistors can operate satisfactorily with their collector-to-emitter voltage a few 10ths of a volt less than their base-to-emitter voltage. This feature can be very useful when it is necessary to operate with a single power supply voltage, in which case the lower supply rail is usually ground.

Internal compensation is provided by the single 30-pF capacitor. It provides roll-off at 6 dB/octave starting at a few hertz and continuing up to approximately the unity gain crossover point around a megahertz, with the slope of the gain characteristic increasing at higher frequencies due to parasitic capacitances and transistor characteristics.

The gain characteristic is essentially the same as that considered optimum throughout this book, and it allows up to 100 percent feedback to be used around the op amp without causing excessive peaking or overshoot. Every opportunity must be exploited fully to start the roll-off at such a low frequency with such a small capacitor. The capacitor is placed in a local feedback loop around a gain stage, so that its value is effectively multiplied by the gain of the stage, because of the Miller effect. The gain of this stage is very high, because of the current source biasing and buffering of subsequent loading, thus enhancing the Miller effect. Finally, the feedback is to a very high impedance point, the junction of two transistor collectors and one base, further increasing the time constant. The capacitor is at the only place meeting all requirements, since feedback around the first stage or both stages would have to go to an input, which would be unsatisfactory.

Advances in Op Amps

Many other improvements have been incorporated in subsequent years, including the use of field-effect transistors for the input pair to get extremely high input impedance and low input bias current. For the latter, the present state of the art is on the order of 3 femtoamps, a mere 20,000 electrons per second. This value is far lower than the old vacuum tube op amps achieved, and so low that the amplifiers are ideal for use with pH electrodes, ionization gauges, photodetectors, and other extremely high impedance sources. Op amps fabricated entirely with complementary field-effect transistors have allowed quiescent power to be reduced to the microwatt range. Input offset drift for some op amps has been reduced to well below 1 $\mu V/°C$, allowing them to replace most chopper stabilized amplifiers. This specification is also truly remarkable, considering that the base emitter voltage drops being canceled by the differential connection are on the order of 600,000 μV, with a temperature sensitivity of about 2000 $\mu V/°C$. The input transistors must be extremely close together, in a region of low thermal gradients, and aligned with an isothermal contour. In addition, the residual input pair differential temperature coefficient can be trimmed by slightly unbalancing the currents in the two transistors, with the resulting offset voltage trimmed back out at a later point in the op amp where temperature coefficient is not a problem. Several other tricks of the trade also minimize temperature coefficient.

Power op amps have been developed with output voltage and current ratings high enough to drive most loads, such as servo motors, directly. Another tremendous advance has been in the area of bandwidth, with so-called video op amps. Some of these are internally connected as buffers with a gain of one or two, and bandwidths of several hundred megahertz. Although designed primarily for video usage, they can be very helpful in feedback loops for buffering without introducing any significant amount of equivalent excess phase.

Op Amp Circuit Analysis

Turning now to the analysis of op amp circuits, two of the outstanding characteristics, very high voltage gain and very high input impedance, make possible an extremely simple approach. Let us look first at a circuit, Fig. 13-3, that sums several inputs and then amplifies and inverts the sum. With the positive input grounded, the voltage at the negative input is the differential input voltage. Because of the high open-loop voltage gain of the op amp, the input voltage will have to be virtually zero for any output within the linear range of the op amp. The output will have to go to the voltage that maintains the input, by virtue of feedback, at virtually 0 V, called a *virtual ground*. Then the current in each input resistor will be simply the voltage applied to that resistor divided by the resistor value, irrespective of voltages applied to the other resistors. Because of the high input impedance and low bias current, we can assume that all this current must continue through the feedback resistor, creating a voltage drop proportional to its value. Since the left end of the feedback resistor is at 0 V, by virtue of connection to a virtual ground, the voltage at the other end, which is the out-

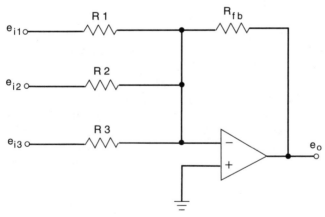

Figure 13-3. Inverting voltage amplifier that sums several inputs.

put voltage of the circuit, is determined. For the top input resistor, we have simply

$$e_o = -(R_{fb}/R1)e_{i1} \qquad (13.1)$$

and similar relations hold for the other two inputs. The same arguments hold, of course, if reactances or complex impedances replace any of the resistors. This feature was exploited to allow writing the gain, or transfer function, of an integrator by inspection in Chap. 4.

The noninverting configuration illustrated in Fig. 13-4 is an example of a complete feedback loop with the op amp's differential input functioning as the comparator, its gain providing the A path, and the two resistors providing the B path. The low frequency gain will be $1/B$, or $(R1 + R2)/R1$, and the dynamic characteristics are determined by the op amp open-loop characteristics, the same as any other feedback loop.

These simple relations are the basic ones needed for the study of feedback loops using op amps, at least as far as the stability problem is concerned. Other important matters, such as the analysis of noise, are covered in application notes provided by manufacturers and in many textbooks, such as (Graeme, Tobey, and Huelsman, 1971).

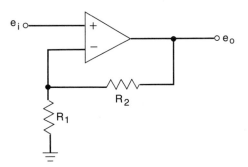

Figure 13-4. Noninverting voltage amplifier.

14
PID Control

"Five Feet High and Rising"—the title of that old country song about flood water reflects appreciation of the importance of rate of change of a variable, as well as its current value. The rate of change, or derivative, is represented by the D in PID, a widely used acronym for Proportional/Integral/Derivative control. In this chapter we take a quick and rather jaundiced look at this subject.

Figure 14-1 is the block diagram of a typical implementation of a PID loop. The main path around the loop provides control proportional to the error between the input and the output, just as in all the loops treated in previous chapters. In addition, the error signal is both integrated and differentiated, and the results, I and D, respectively, are added to the proportional signal P to give a modified control signal that is supposed to improve performance.

As a preliminary, we need to consider how the addition of the P, I, and D signals at the second summing junction affects the loop gain.

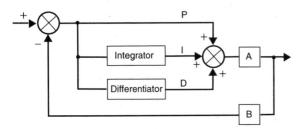

Figure 14-1. Typical Proportional/Integral/Derivative loop.

When elements are cascaded, the logarithmic gains add, but this will not be the case when signals are added. For this discussion, it will suffice to note, qualitatively, that the output at any frequency will be essentially the same as any input that is by far the largest at that frequency. Since the amplitude of the I and D signals increases without bound at very low and very high frequencies, respectively, these signals will control performance in those regions, while the P signal will prevail in the midfrequency range. For the first summing junction, present in all loops, the same question doesn't arise. As far as the loop gain is concerned, the gain through that summing junction is simply minus one.

The Integral Signal

Looking first at the integral signal, it is often obtained from an op amp integrator as shown in Fig. 4-3. Since this circuit inverts as well as integrates, the output would be subtracted, rather than added at the second summing junction. The ostensible purpose of this signal is to reduce the steady-state error to zero, in effect converting a type 0 loop to a type 1 loop. Actually, only the component of error due to finite loop gain is reduced to zero, while another component due to offsets in amplifiers and/or sensors remains. If the low-frequency loop gain, though finite, is sufficient to reduce the first error to less than the second, any further increase in gain serves no useful purpose. With modern op amps having gains approaching 1,000,000, it is rarely necessary or advantageous to include integration.

In addition, the zero-frequency or steady-state error is a rather meaningless concept in the first place. It applies only when the input and all disturbances have been constant forever, a state of affairs which cannot occur very often for any given system, to put it mildly, and one in which a feedback control system is hardly needed. Far more important than the zero-frequency gain is the gain in the regions of the frequency spectrum where the input or disturbances have substantial amplitude.

If system specifications require a value of A_o that can not be obtained readily with a single op amp, it is sometimes possible to cascade two closed loops to reduce the demand on A_o. If that approach is not practical, an alternative is to use two cascaded op amps in the forward path, with local feedback around the second, a video type, to give an additional factor of 10 or 100 in gain, with time constants that are too small to be troublesome. This solution usually requires a phase retard network also to start the roll-off earlier so that conditions around the crossover frequency stay the same. If necessary, even higher values of low-frequency loop gain can be obtained with cascaded op amps, using compensation techniques discussed at the end of Chap. 11. The slope of -9 dB/octave employed there is particularly appropriate when the low-frequency gain must be unusually high. Where practical, this is much better use of an op amp than using it to implement an integrator.

Besides being unnecessary in most cases, integration introduces a very objectionable problem stemming from the fact that every definite integral includes an arbitrary constant. In an op amp integrator, this constant appears as a charge on the capacitor that can result from turn-on transients, power supply glitches, or overload conditions. Such a charge results in a protracted output error until the error has been integrated long enough to eliminate the charge. Although various manual and more or less automatic schemes have been devised to initialize or reset integrators to deal with this problem, good practice now exploits the high gain and great bandwidth of modern op amps to reduce low-frequency error sufficiently without recourse to integration. The deliberate use of integration is an anachronism dating to the days when available op amp gains were woefully low.

The Derivative Signal

The derivative signal will be negligible at low frequency but will increase the loop gain by 6 dB/octave at high and perhaps midfrequencies. Therefore, it can serve very much the same as a phase advance network in helping to achieve an optimum open-loop gain characteristic. However, the key question is, What improvement in the desired open-loop gain characteristic does the availability of a derivative signal make possible? The answer is none. Phase advance networks, as discussed in Chap. 11 on loop compensation, provide any desirable augmentation of high-frequency gain, are simpler, and do not introduce the problem of excessive high-frequency noise that is inherent with differentiators.

If desired, a phase advance network can be looked at as providing a derivative signal over a limited frequency range. However, this concept is unnecessary and is a bit queasy from a mathematical standpoint. The analogous view-point for a phase retard network is that it is an integrator over a limited frequency range, but this concept is equally unnecessary.

Summary

Our discussion of the recombination of the P, I, and D signals at the second summing junction was somewhat oversimplified, and thus obscured some possibilities for achieving slightly better performance with more sophisticated recombination schemes. Such methods have been used mainly for complicated process control loops, which usually have significant time delays. These methods are rarely used for, or appropriate for, most ordinary feedback loops up through a moderate level of complexity. Furthermore, there is no way to eliminate completely the objectional characteristics of the I and D signals. Therefore, we will conclude that it is usually best to avoid PID control for most loops, especially when, as is usually the case, any desired amount of low frequency gain can be provided very easily with one or two op amps.

15
Complications

In this chapter we discuss a few miscellaneous complications that are frequently encountered when working with feedback loops, starting with resonance.

Resonance

There is an old saying among electrical engineers that if you want an oscillator, design an amplifier, and vice versa. The saying stems from the observation that new oscillator designs are frequently reluctant to oscillate, while new amplifier designs are frequently prone to, suggesting that oscillators and amplifiers may be quite similar. Many oscillator designs comprise amplification and a frequency selective element, either a resonance or an antiresonance, connected in a loop. Thus all feedback loops with a frequency selective element are very similar and may have a strong tendency to oscillate. Furthermore, if the loop gain is high, the resonance need not be very sharp. Many oscillators use a twin-T network as the frequency selective element, and it has an equivalent Q of only 0.25 (Valley and Wallman, 1948, p. 394).

One way of dealing with a resonance, either electrical or mechanical, is to cancel its effect with an electrical antiresonance of the same center frequency and Q in the forward path. Frequently the easiest way to implement antiresonance is with an active RC circuit of the type shown in many op amp application handbooks. This type of compensation works well, of course, only when both the center frequency and Q of the resonance are quite stable. Otherwise, the parameters of the antiresonance could, in principle, be adjusted somehow to track those of the resonance, but that approach gets into the area of adaptive control systems, which is beyond the scope of this book.

Another way of dealing with a resonance in a loop is to reduce its Q by damping it in some way. Best of all, however, is to simply eliminate the resonance completely. In electrical circuits capacitors are almost inevitable, so inductors should be avoided as far as possible. Similarly, in mechanical mechanisms, masses are inevitable, so springs should be avoided if possible. In particular, use of springs to provide a restoring force should be eliminated by providing positive drive in both directions. Compressible gas in pneumatic devices, or air bubbles in hydraulic systems, should be avoided like the plague. When unavoidable, as in air brake systems, gas introduces another major time constant, so the characteristics of the rest of the loop must be controlled even more carefully than usual.

Nonlinearities

Nonlinearities are generally beyond the scope of this book. However, minor nonlinearities in the forward path, such as crossover distortion in a complementary emitter follower, or modest nonlinearity in the gain of an op amp can be virtually eliminated by feedback without requiring much attention as far as loop analysis goes. In some other instances more serious nonlinearities can be dealt with very easily by compensating them, very much as a resonance can be compensated with an antiresonance. The most common example of this situation is a temperature controller utilizing a resistor as a heater. The error signal causes a proportional voltage across the resistor, but the resulting heating is proportional to the square of that voltage, a nonlinear relationship. The effect is to increase the incremental open-loop gain at high heating with a concomitant decrease in stability. Any overshoot at all is very undesirable, since there is no ability to cool, so control will be lost completely until things cool down on their own, which might take a long time. Therefore, the gain must be set quite low to ensure no overshoot even when heating is at its maximum. This setting results in sloppy control and sluggish response when the heating is low.

This type of nonlinearity can be compensated very simply by introducing another nonlinear transfer function, namely, a square root function, ahead of it, as shown in Fig. 15-1. This function can be an analog module or a digital signal processor, although the latter would not usually be practical in a simple system where the signals are not digitized otherwise. For many simple requirements the processing can be achieved extremely simply with only a diode and a few resistors, plus

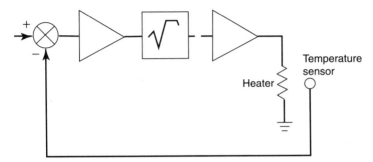

Figure 15-1. Temperature control loop with compensating nonlinearity in forward path.

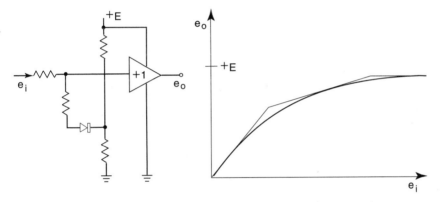

Figure 15-2. Simple approximation of square root function.

the voltage limiting imposed by the power supply. Figure 15-2 shows a circuit and the resulting three-segment approximation to a square root function. Although crude, it is good enough to greatly improve the performance of a temperature controller.

Log Conversion

Another commonly encountered nonlinearity in feedback loops is a log function, introduced deliberately to create a log conversion circuit. The inherent characteristics of bipolar transistors are the basis for the logarithmic relation, and the transistors must be used in a feedback loop to exploit their characteristics effectively. The two most common configurations are shown, in rudimentary form, in Fig. 15-3. A dy-

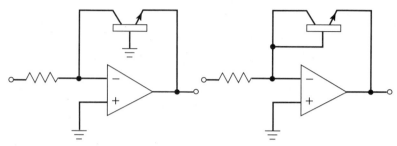

Figure 15-3. Rudimentary log converter circuits.

namic range of about 6 decades or more of input current or voltage can be achieved with good accuracy. If the input is a current, the input resistors shown are omitted. Both cases require temperature control or sophisticated thermal compensation techniques but we will not get into the details, since we are concerned here mainly with the loop stability problem. In the circuit on the left, the logging transistor constitutes a common base gain stage that is the B, or feedback, path in the loop. Its transconductance is proportional to collector current, so its gain, and hence the loop gain, can vary over 1,000,000 to 1 range, depending on the input signal.

At first glance the circuit on the right might seem to avoid this problem, since the transistor is connected as a diode and hence cannot provide voltage gain. However, the dynamic impedance of the connection varies inversely as the current; therefore, the feedback factor, and hence the loop gain, changes over the same tremendous range. If the signal is coming from a current source, which is often the case with these circuits, capacitance at the amplifier input, in conjunction with the dynamic impedance of the diode connected transistor, constitutes a lag whose time constant varies over the same range.

The tendency to instability is worst at maximum current for both configurations. A capacitor is frequently used around the op amp to provide adequate stability at maximum current, but the price is slow response at low currents. Better performance can be realized by adding a resistor, as shown in Fig. 15-4, allowing a smaller capacitor to suffice. The output must still be taken from a terminal of the logging transistor, with buffering if necessary, although that is not shown.

It seems plausible that we could exploit a compensating nonlinearity in the loop to keep the open-loop gain more fixed, as in the example with a heater, and it could serve a useful purpose, up to a point. However, when making a measurement, as in this instance, signal-to-noise ratio always deteriorates at low levels, so it may be desirable to

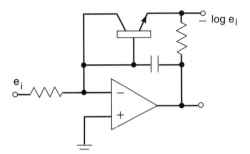

Figure 15-4. Stabilization of log converter circuit.

have the frequency response of the measuring system decrease at low levels also. The effect is to low-pass filter the measured signal with a filter whose cutoff frequency decreases as the signal level goes down, thus keeping the signal-to-noise ratio from dropping too much. We wind up with an adaptive circuit, in effect, without even trying.

For the circuit on the right in Fig. 15-3, the Johnson noise of the logging element varies as the square root of its dynamic resistance, which in turn varies inversely with current. Thus a source of noise in the measuring system increases as the signal decreases. The circuit on the left would behave in a similar fashion, although the explanation is not as obvious. The equivalent input noise voltage and current of the op amp are also factors for both circuits, of course. In addition, the signal-to-noise ratio of the source will inevitably decrease at low levels. If the source is a photosensor, for example, the statistics of the arrival of photons will cause the decrease. All these factors must be considered when deciding on the desired closed-loop response.

ac Coupling

Next we consider the problem of ac coupling within a loop. This problem is quite rare now but was common back in the vacuum tube era because of the need to use capacitors between most stages to block the large bias offset voltages. When feedback was used around several stages, and perhaps an output transformer as well, this frequently caused instability in the form of low-frequency oscillation. In the case of audio amplifiers, the resulting sound emanating from the loud speaker caused this condition to be called "motorboating." Nowadays, when ac coupling is necessary or desirable, it can usually be achieved with a blocking capacitor just ahead of a direct coupled loop if the signal spectrum does not extend all the way to zero. If both the signal spectrum and the disturbance spectrum do not go to zero, a blocking capacitor between the output of a direct coupled loop and the load is an alternative. In some cases it might be desirable to use capacitors both before and after the direct coupled loop. In all these cases the ac coupling does not affect the stability of the loop.

If one or two blocking capacitors, or equivalent elements, must be included within a loop, the low-frequency stability problem becomes almost identical to the high-frequency problem normally considered and requires the same control of phase at the low-frequency unity gain frequency. No problems occur if the loop has only one capacitor, just as with the first-order systems treated in Chap. 8. If the loop has two capacitors, stability depends on the ratio of the time constants and the midband open-loop gain, as shown in Chap. 9.

The main difference between the low-frequency and the high-frequency stability problems is that excess phase from transport lags is not a problem at low frequencies. In fact, such phase shift would help, since it is of the opposite polarity to the phase shift of the blocking capacitors, causing partial cancellation. However, the phase shift from the amount of delay that could be tolerated at high frequencies without damaging stability excessively would be completely negligible at low frequencies, since the shift is proportional to frequency.

Impedance Matching

Another problem occasionally encountered is that of obtaining a prescribed output impedance. Although not one of the more important applications of feedback, this problem is interesting for its novelty. Matching the output impedance of a driver to the characteristic impedance of a transmission line will reduce multiple reflections if the load at the other end is not perfectly matched. For video lines, for example, a common approach is to use an op amp with 50 percent feedback, to give a closed loop gain of two, as well as output impedance that is negligible compared to 75 Ω, and then to follow the op amp with a 75-Ω resistor. While this approach is acceptable for video and other communication links, it is not so good for higher power situations, because the matching resistor must dissipate as much power as is delivered to the load and the driving amplifier must furnish twice the power delivered to the load. To avoid this situation, feedback can be utilized in a slightly more complex fashion to set the output impedance to any desired value, with minimal dissipation in the driving circuit except for a very small amount in a current-sensing resistor. The approach has been used to power incandescent lamps used in spectrophotometers. In this case the goal is not to eliminate reflections, but rather to make the power delivered to the lamp independent of small changes in filament resistance. Neither a constant voltage nor a constant current source will ensure constant power, since $P = E^2/R = I^2R$. However, a source whose output impedance is equal to the filament resistance at its operating point will suffice because shifts in operating point caused by slight changes in filament resistance will lie on a hyperbola representing constant power, as shown in Fig. 15-5. Another way to see the benefit of impedance matching is to take the partial derivative of the power delivered to the load P with respect to the load resistance R_L. Denoting the source resistance by R_g and the source voltage by E, we have $I = E/(R_g + R_L)$, so that $P = I^2R_L = E^2R_L/(R_g + R_L)^2$. Then

$$(\partial P)/(\partial R_L) = E^2[(R_g + R_L)^2 - 2R_L(R_g + R_L)]/(R_g + R_L)^4 \qquad (15.1)$$

The partial derivative will be zero only if $R_g = R_L$, which can be verified by substituting into Eq. (15.1).

In Fig. 15-6, R_L represents the lamp or load resistance, and R_s is a current-sensing resistor. For the sake of concreteness, some realistic component values are shown. The lamp is a quartz-iodine type operating at 100 V, 100 W, and 1 Å. If R2 is temporarily removed from the cir-

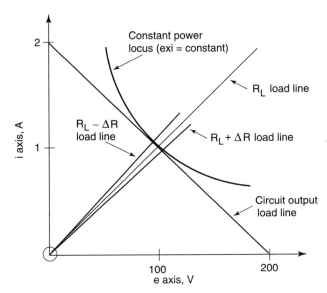

Figure 15-5. Load lines for circuit of Fig. 15-6 when source and load impedances are approximately matched.

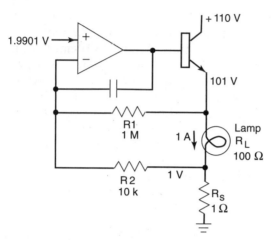

Figure 15-6. Low dissipation driver circuit with output impedance matching load impedance.

cuit, the driver becomes a constant voltage source with virtually zero output impedance, so an increase in lamp resistance will cause a decrease in power. Conversely, if $R1$ is removed, with $R2$ replaced, the driver becomes a current source with nominally infinite output impedance. Under these conditions an increase in lamp resistance will cause an increase in power. A condition halfway between these extremes will make the lamp power constant despite small changes in filament resistance. This state requires equal contributions to the feedback by the voltage sensing and the current sensing, calling for the ratio of the feedback resistors to be the same as the ratio of the lamp resistance to the current-sensing resistor. The value of R_s is arbitrary, but it should be much smaller than R_L to avoid wasting power and, more important, so that R_s doesn't heat up excessively, which would adversely affect the stability of its value. In this example the dissipation is 1 W, so a parallel combination of 10 precision resistors, each 10 Ω, $\frac{1}{2}$ W rating, is appropriate. If R_s is too small, parasitic resistance, amplifier input offset drift, or thermoelectric potentials may become problems. Thanks to the high input impedance of the op amp, the feedback resistors can be large enough to make any loading effect on the current-sensing resistor completely negligible.

It would be well to check that the preceding resistor values will result in proper operation. Under the conditions shown, the feedback voltage at the inverting input of the op amp can be found easily with the aid of the superposition theorem as applied in Eq. (15.2).

$$e_{fb} = 101(10k)/(10k + 1M) + 1(1M)/(10k + 1M) \qquad (15.2)$$
$$= 101(0.009901) + 1(0.9901)$$
$$= 1 + 0.9901$$
$$= 1.9901$$

Now suppose that the lamp resistance increases to 102 Ω. If the voltage across it stayed at 100 V, the power would decrease by 2 percent, so an increase in voltage of 1 percent is needed to hold the power constant, since power varies as the square of the voltage. The combination of a 1 percent increase in voltage and a 2 percent increase in lamp resistance causes a 1 percent decrease in current to 0.99 Å. Under the new conditions we have Eq. (15.3).

$$e_{fb} = 102(0.009901) + 0.99(0.9901) \qquad (15.3)$$
$$= 1.9901$$

Since e_i would be unchanged and the feedback voltage must be equal to it, the unchanged value of feedback voltage confirms that the change in output voltage resulting from the combined voltage and current feedback with the resistor values shown is exactly what is needed to maintain constant power. The reader who is uncomfortable with the rather heuristic analysis used here should feel free to write circuit equations, solve for the power in the lamp, and show that it is independent of slight changes in lamp resistance.

The extreme simplicity of the circuit results in part from being able to float the load, meaning that neither lamp terminal needs to be grounded, thus allowing one end of the current-sensing resistor to be grounded. This approach is not possible if the load is an unbalanced transmission line such as a coaxial cable.

Finally we come to the matter of stabilization. Assuming that the op amp is internally compensated for 100 percent feedback, the single capacitor shown, if large enough, will assure loop stability irrespective of the characteristics of the lamp, which would have a thermal time constant, and the emitter follower, which would probably be a power Darlington with dubious and unknown high-frequency characteristics. The capacitor short circuits the overall feedback at high frequencies, thus eliminating the stability problem if the op amp internal compensation is satisfactory for 100 percent feedback. The value of capacitance needed can be determined experimentally with much less effort than would be needed to determine the frequency domain characteristics of the transistor and lamp, information which would be needed for a more sophisticated approach to stabilization.

This quick and dirty approach is often overlooked, but it may be ideal for special cases such as this example in which feedback control is needed mainly to cope with low-frequency disturbances. This situation also benefits from the fact that as the capacitor takes over at high frequencies, the circuit becomes essentially a constant voltage source, which is not too far removed from our goal.

The method just discussed for minimizing light fluctuations is only one of many possible approaches. The same scheme can be implemented to good advantage with a computer, which would simply calculate the power by multiplying measured current and applied voltage and adjusting the latter to obtain the desired power. With the computer, taking the square root to linearize the system becomes extremely simple, as discussed above, although this factor is not too important when only small changes are expected.

Of course, light output is not completely controlled, since the lamp efficiency is assumed to be constant, but may not be exactly. Regulating the power will help to maintain constant efficiency, but some variation could still occur. To include this variation, we can split off and measure a small fraction of the light beam before it passes through the spectrophotometer and divide the final reading by the reference reading. This technique not only corrects for changes in power and efficiency but also eliminates the need to regulate the light output, and does it without feedback, thereby eliminating the stability problem as well. However, this approach has its own problems, such as increased electrical, optical, and signal processing complexity and additional drift from the second light detector. The latter could be eliminated by timesharing a single detector, but then you have the complexity, stability, and speed of the optical multiplexing system to worry about. As is usually the case, the optimum solution depends on the details of each situation and may not be the same for all.

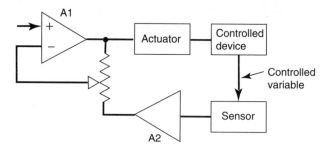

Figure 15-7. Circuit allowing feedback factor to be varied without drastically changing overall gain.

Adjusting the Feedback Factor

As a final example we consider the occasional requirement to be able to vary the feedback all the way down to zero without changing the low-frequency characteristics of the system excessively. This requirement is simple to achieve with the configuration shown in Fig. 15-7. For this scheme to work satisfactorily, no integration can occur in the portion of the system to the right of the potentiometer, and the gain of $A2$ must be properly adjusted relative to the actuator.

16
Transport Lags

Up to this point we have focused almost exclusively on linear minimum phase loops. Transport lags and nonlinearities are the principal factors that degrade performance and complicate analysis significantly in more complex loops. As we have seen, in many cases feedback can reduce the effect of nonlinearities, and in others it can be compensated relatively simply by introducing other nonlinearities. Nevertheless, nonlinearities in general require difficult analytical methods that are beyond the scope of this book. Transport lags, on the other hand, can be handled fairly easily with the methods developed previously, suitably extended, and these methods prove to be the simplest and easiest for the task.

Ironically, perhaps, a study of transport lags is also desirable in connection with minimum phase loops for two reasons. One is indirect. Increased attention to transport lags helps the designer eliminate or minimize them so that the benefits of minimum phase can be realized as fully as possible. The other reason relates to minimum phase loops with more than three time constants. To have reasonable closed-loop stability, all open-loop time constants in excess of three, after appropriate compensation, must be so short that their effect will be the same as that of transport lags, as discussed in Chap. 6. Consequently, the ability to deal with transport lags provides the ability to deal with minimum phase loops with any number of time constants.

Nature and Effect of Transport Lags

To begin, we review the distinction between a transport lag and the lag characteristic discussed in Chap. 3. Both retard the phase of a sinusoidal signal, although in different fashions, as shown in Fig. 6-8, but a lag also attenuates the signal, while a transport lag does not. The fundamental cause of a transport lag is flow or propagation. An everyday example of a transport lag in a feedback loop is a shower. The transport lag is the time it takes the water to go up the pipe from the faucets to the shower head and onto the person taking the shower. If the water coming out is too cold, the resulting error signal will cause the input temperature to be raised, but there will be no immediate increase in output temperature, so the input may be further increased excessively. Then when the temperature finally goes up, it will be too hot, leading to a repetition in the opposite direction. This sequence could go on indefinitely, resulting in oscillation as a result of the transport lag. In the real world, oscillation usually does not occur, thanks to a powerful signal processor in the loop. That, of course, is a human brain, which has been described as the most sophisticated signal processing device that can be mass produced by unskilled labor. It uses several methods to avoid instability, one of which is to make a small correction and then wait until the transport time, which has been ascertained by experience, has elapsed before utilizing the feedback for further correction. A similar stabilizing effect could occur in a sampled data system if the sampling interval exceeds the transport time and the maximum correction after each sampling is restricted. This pattern suggests the reason that sampled data systems are sometimes more tolerant of transport lags than the continuous systems considered in this book. Of course, there is a big price to be paid in that sampled data systems cannot respond to inputs or disturbances as rapidly. Since sampled data feedback systems are beyond the scope of this book, we will not get into this topic further.

No amount of effort devoted to sophisticated analysis can undo the destabilizing effect of a transport lag. The most strenuous effort should be applied, instead, to reducing the transport lag. In a water bath temperature controller, for example, the distance from the heater to the temperature sensor should be reduced to a bare minimum. If the two sites are connected by tubing, small tubing with a high flow velocity will introduce less transport lag than big tubing with a low flow velocity. If there is no flow at all, but the heat travels via thermal diffusion, there is still excess phase, or at least equivalent excess phase as discussed in Chap. 6. As another example, if communication links in either the forward or feedback paths are introducing delays, the links should be modified to virtually eliminate the delays. There is no good reason why information flow should not approach the speed of light, resulting in negligible delay in any reasonably compact system. If the signal is digitized, within a loop, sigma-delta type analog-to-digital converters should be avoided, because they introduce a delay.

Transport lags that cannot be eliminated result in excess phase that is proportional to the transport time and to frequency. Because the excess phase exerts its greatest influence near the open-loop unity gain crossover frequency, lowering that frequency can reduce the effect of the transport lag. Of course, impaired system responsivity is the trade-off for improved stability. The only other viable remedy is to use phase advance around the crossover frequency to help hold down the total phase shift. Bode plots of both gain and phase give a good picture of what is going on. Due to the exponential shape of the phase shift of a transport lag on a Bode plot, the unity gain crossover frequency cannot be much above the frequency where the exponential takes off. If we take this point, somewhat arbitrarily, as the frequency where the phase shift due to the transport lag is 10°, then Eq. (6.1) indicates that the unity gain crossover frequency should not exceed about $1/(36\tau)$, where τ is the delay in seconds.

Turning now from general observations to specific examples, we start with a first-order loop, which was found in Chap. 8 to have an open-loop phase of $-90°$ at the unity gain crossover frequency. The value of delay τ that causes an additional 90° of phase shift at the open-loop unity gain frequency f_c, increases the total phase shift to 360°, which results in sustained oscillation, and is thus an upper limit that should not be approached too closely. The open-loop unity gain frequency is $A_0 B/2\pi T$, and the phase shift caused by the delay is 360 $f\tau°$. Setting the latter equal to 90° gives $\tau = 1/(4f_c)$, or, using the equation for unity gain frequency as well, $\tau = \pi T/(2A_0 B)$.

Computer Simulation of a Transport Lag

The degree of stability with other values of τ, and for second-order systems with a transport lag, can be investigated most easily with SPICE simulations, using the system of Fig. 16-1. For these simulations the closed-loop gain was arbitrarily set at 10, and the low-frequency open-loop gain was set at 1000, with roll-off starting at 160 Hz so that the unity gain crossover frequency at which excess phase is calculated is 160 kHz. The various values of transport lag are simulated by a properly terminated lossless transmission line. The value of the capacitor in the second lag was varied to give the different values of gain at the -6 to -12 dB/octave transition point. The resulting values of

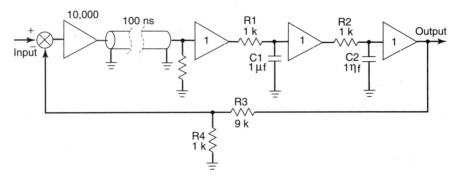

Figure 16-1. Schematic used for computer simulations of loops with two time constants and a transport lag.

overshoot with a step function input, and peaking, appear in Figs. 16-2 and 16-3, respectively. Excess phase, rather than phase margin, has been used for the x axis, since the latter will be different for the different curves before the excess phase of the transport lag is added in. Use of phase, rather than delay, normalizes the curves for any loop. The excess phase in degrees is 360 times the product of transport delay and the unity gain frequency, which has been based on the longer time constant without taking into account the effect of the other time constant. This effect will be slight except when the transition to a -12 dB/octave slope occurs at positive gain, but the transition cannot be at a gain much above 0 dB if there is much transport lag without impairing stability excessively.

In Figs. 16-2 and 16-3, the extreme right-hand curve is for a first-order system. These curves show that the 90° phase margin of a first-order loop without a transport lag is more than enough to provide freedom from both peaking and overshoot, answering a question that arose in Chap. 8. Increasing the delay above a threshold value causes peaking and overshoot to increase slowly at first and then more rapidly, approaching infinity as the phase margin approaches zero.

Conditional Stability

Still greater values of delay, giving negative phase margin, result in stable operation again, but the stability is only conditional. A momentary reduction in either loop gain or transport lag can cause oscillation to set in, and it may continue even after conditions return to normal, as discussed in Chap. 10. This possibility is so undesirable that the

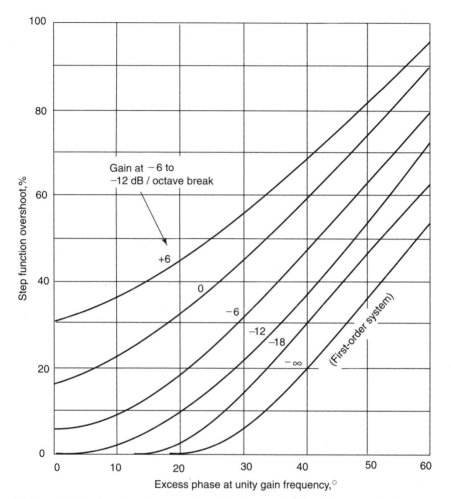

Figure 16-2. Step function overshoot for loops with two time constants as a function of excess phase at the unity gain frequency.

design curves encompass only values of excess phase that usually will not make the phase margin negative.

It should not be assumed, however, that conditionally stable feedback loops do not exist or that they cannot function reasonably satisfactorily in some situations. Sound systems are a common example of loops that may be in a conditionally stable state sometimes. Although not intended to be feedback systems, they inevitably are due to sound propagation at 1100 ft/s from the loudspeaker back to the microphone. If the distance is about 25 ft, the excess phase will exceed 90° by 10 Hz

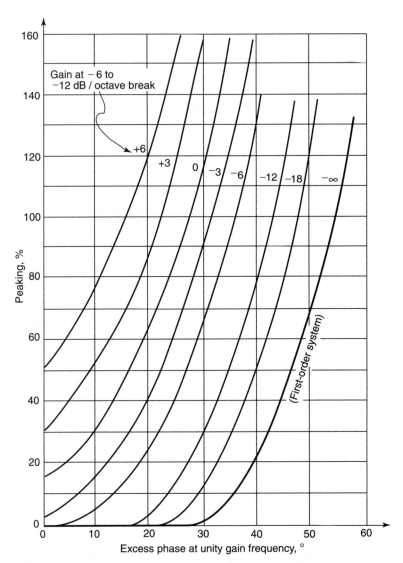

Figure 16-3. Peaking for loops with two time constants as a function of excess phase at the unity gain frequency.

and will be tens of thousands of degrees at several kHz. The unity gain frequency must be positioned between two of the many frequencies at which the excess phase makes the total open loop phase an integral multiple of 360°. The stability here might seem precarious, especially if a portable mike is in use. The phase at about 1000 Hz where sound systems usually tend to oscillate, changes 180° for every $\frac{1}{2}$-ft change in spacing between the speaker and the microphone. The saving grace is that the loop gain is very low compared to the loops we have been studying, thanks to nonfrequency-dependent attenuation roughly proportional to the square of the distance and other factors. In addition, the system often has an equalizer, which, although ostensibly for tone control, can also provide loop compensation with a great deal of flexibility, and the compensation can be set up and readjusted if necessary in real time under the exact conditions prevailing.

It is quite possible that some physiological control loops that involve transport via blood flow, or other circulation, are conditionally stable. That state should be considered a possibility for any feedback loop that includes a large transport lag, especially if the loop is prone to exhibit erratic behavior occasionally, such as howling in a sound system.

Ripple above the break frequency in the closed-loop Bode gain plot, although rarely seen, is a sure indicator of a large transport lag causing a substantially negative phase margin. A rather extreme case is illustrated in Fig. 16-4. The ripples have a fixed frequency spacing and result from the open-loop phase repeatedly changing from exactly in phase to exactly out of phase and back with each 360° increase in phase as the frequency increases. The delay is the reciprocal of the difference in frequency between successive peaks, and vice versa. The amplitude of the ripples decreases with increasing frequency because of the reduction in loop gain caused by one or more time constants.

Rise Time

The rise time of the step function response will not be affected markedly by the decrease in stability due to the delay, as discussed in Chap. 12, but the rise will be delayed if the transport lag is in the A path. There will also be ringing after the main response, and it will die out more slowly as the phase margin approaches zero. In general, the ringing caused by a step function input will become unacceptable well before the phase margin reaches zero and will remain unacceptable for any negative value of phase margin, even though that state might be acceptable with inputs that do not change as rapidly as a step function.

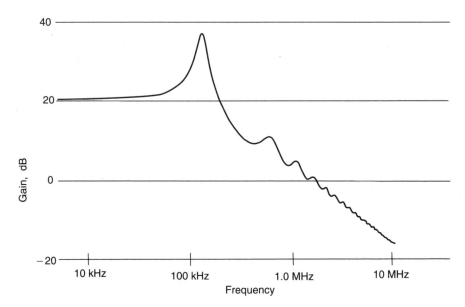

Figure 16-4. Closed-loop gain plot indicating conditional stability as the result of a large transport lag.

Use of Phase Advance

Figure 16-5 illustrates the beneficial effect of phase advance. The upper curve is for a second-order system with a very small transport lag and the gain at the −6 to −12 dB/octave transition point about + 3 dB, resulting in step function overshoot of about 34 percent, before any phase advance was used. The lower curve is for the same system, except with a much larger transport lag, and the gain at the −6 to −12 dB/octave transition about −9 dB; the step function overshoot without any phase advance was about the same, 32 percent. As the capacitance around the feedback resistor was increased from zero to provide phase advance, the overshoot was reduced to zero in both cases. Surprisingly, perhaps, the reduction is about twice as fast for the loop with the larger transport lag, which can be attributed to the much better stability of that loop except for the transport lag.

Computer Simulation of Third-Order Loop with a Transport Lag

At this point we have developed tools to deal with first-through third-order minimum phase loops, and first- and second-order loops with a

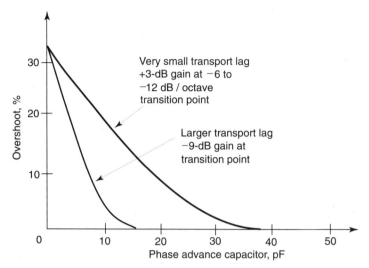

Figure 16-5. Effect of phase advance on overshoot.

transport lag. We still need tools for fourth- and higher-order minimum phase loops and for third- and higher-order loops with a transport lag. These tools can best be developed with computer simulations similar to those used for second-order loops with a transport lag. However, the number of variables would call for either multidimensional graphs to depict the results or many two-dimensional graphs. To avoid this situation, we will content ourselves with additional graphs for only one special third-order system with a transport lag. Interpolation between these curves and those for a second-order system with a transport lag will allow us to obtain results for any third-order system with a transport lag, and also for all higher-order loops, with or without a transport lag.

Computer simulations were performed on the system shown in Fig. 16-1 with one more buffered lag network added, with its time constant held the same as the time constant of the last lag of the original loop. The Bode gain plot for this loop is the bottom curve of Fig. 16-6. It is a special third-order system in that the second and third break frequencies coincide, resulting in a change of slope directly from −6 to −18 dB/octave without an intermediate segment at −12 dB/octave. The top curve in this figure is for the second-order loop simulated previously. The curve in the middle is the general third-order characteristic we want to analyze. Numerical results for the general curve can be obtained by interpolating between the results for the top and bottom curves, based on how far the third break frequency of the general

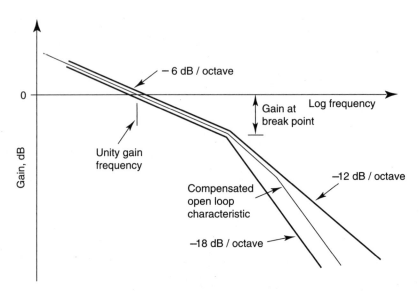

Figure 16-6. Bode plots for use in estimating overshoot for loops with three time constants and a transport lag.

curve is above the second break frequency. This process should probably be called "estimation" rather than *interpolation*, but it will usually provide adequate accuracy. Moderately accurate performance predictions with known inputs are usually adequate because of the ambiguous character of the inputs and disturbances that are encountered in actual operation.

Figures 16-7 and 16-8 give the step function overshoot and peaking, respectively, for third-order loops with a transport lag, for the special case where the two shortest time constants are equal. They are analogous to Figs. 16-2 and 16-3 for second-order loops with a transport lag. Values of peaking or overshoot for general third-order systems lie between the values given by the two sets of curves and can be estimated reasonably well as just discussed. The most interesting feature of Fig. 16-7 is that all the curves are fairly straight and parallel, with a slope of roughly 1.2 percent overshoot for each degree of excess phase at the open-loop unity gain crossover frequency. This factor also applies quite well to the curves of Fig. 16-2 for first- and second-order systems, thus providing an extremely simple way to take into account the effect of a transport lag on step function overshoot.

Both sets of curves show that peaking increases much more rapidly than overshoot as excess phase increases. Similar behavior was noted

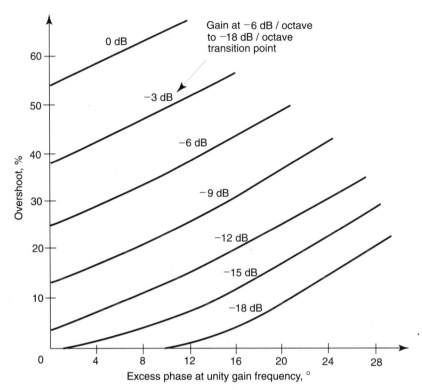

Figure 16-7. Overshoot as a function of excess phase at the unity gain frequency for the bottom curve of Fig. 16-6.

earlier for minimum phase loops as the ratio of time constants decreases.

The destabilizing effect of a transport lag is shown graphically in Figs. 16-9 and 16-10. Conditions are identical except for the transport lag added for Fig. 16-10. The delay in the rise is clearly evident, as well as the greatly increased ringing. The rise time is not affected very much, however.

Methods for Handling Transport Lags

Several methods of determining peaking and overshoot when a transport lag is present have been developed in this chapter. The simplest approach for determining overshoot approximately is to just augment

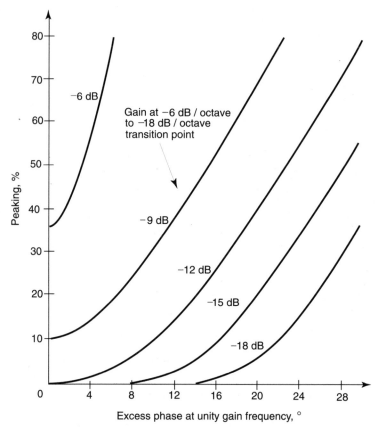

Figure 16-8. Peaking as a function of excess phase at the unity gain frequency for the bottom curve of Fig. 16-6.

the overshoot determined without considering the transport lag by 1.2 percent for each degree of excess phase at the unity gain frequency. For slightly better accuracy, or to find peaking, the simplest approach for most first- or second-order loops is to use the curves of Figs. 16-2 and 16-3. A Bode gain plot is used to carry out loop compensation and to determine the open-loop unity gain frequency to be used in calculating the excess phase caused by the transport lag. When the system has three major time constants and a transport lag, performance can be estimated from the curves developed for second- and third-order systems with a transport lag. With all these approaches any number of higher-order time constants are treated as additional transport lag.

If there is significant excess phase that is not a linear function of frequency, the time has probably come to abandon elementary methods

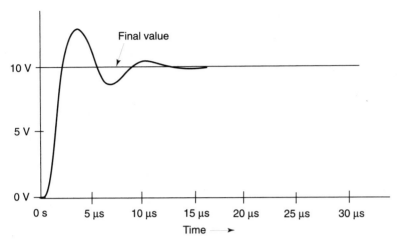

Figure 16-9. Step function response of typical second-order loop without a transport lag

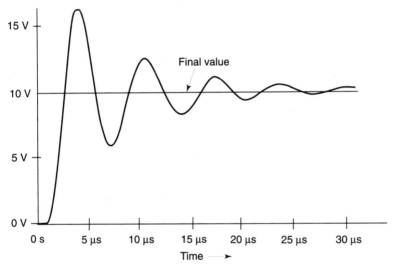

Figure 16-10. Step function response of typical second-order loop with a transport lag.

and turn to SPICE for direct simulation of the specific loop in question. This approach is very powerful because SPICE can accommodate hysteresis, diffusion, and the like, as well as delay. However, this shift in approach entails considerable loss of convenience and flexibility and is not a step to take too soon. Nevertheless, the step ultimately has to be taken at some level of complexity, and this level might be appropriate.

This approach is apt to be the best for handling major nonlinearities also.

Effect of Input Rise Time on Loop Performance

Turning now to a different subject that needs to be slipped in somewhere, we mentioned back in Chap. 8 that a step function is not always a very realistic test signal. Since we have SPICE running and set up for transient analysis, we will take another look at this matter, even though it is not related exclusively to transport lags. Figure 16-11 shows the response of the loop of Fig. 16-1 with two different inputs: a step function with zero rise time and a ramp input with a rise time of about 5 μs. The circuit parameters were selected so that the step function overshoot without a transport lag would have been very slight, but a transport lag of about ½ μs increases the overshoot with the step input to about 35 percent. The output rise time with a step input is

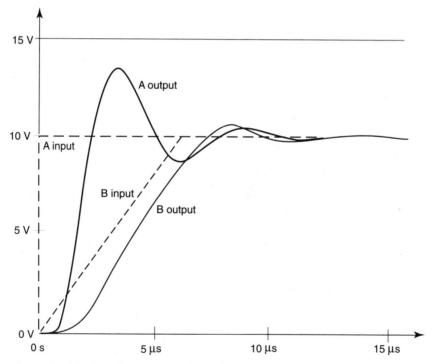

Figure 16-11. Step function responses for two inputs with different rise times.

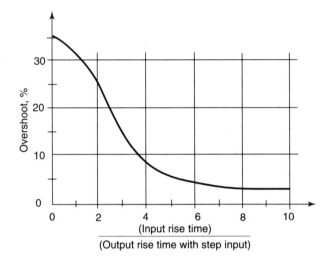

Figure 16-12. Dependence of overshoot on input rise time for a typical loop.

about 1 μs with the parameters mentioned. It is instructive to look at the overshoot plotted against the ratio of the input rise time to the output rise time with a step input. The input rise time for a ramp is 0.8 times the total ramp time. The results appear in Fig. 16-12. Although this figure is based on a specific loop characteristic, the results with most reasonably stable loops will be fairly similar. Increasing the rise time of the input reduces the overshoot markedly, with most of the improvement coming by the time the input rise time is about three times the system rise time with a step input. Looking at it the other way, this point is when the system is three times faster than the input, which is approximately the requirement to avoid degrading the rise time of inputs significantly, since cascaded rise times combine approximately as the square root of the sum of the squares. Thus, overshoot with the fastest inputs a loop should be expected to handle properly in regard to rise time will be substantially less than the overshoot with a step function input.

This consideration, along with, in most cases, limited knowledge of the exact characteristics of the inputs and disturbances to be expected, suggests that excessive effort expended to achieve high accuracy in design or analysis may not be very cost-effective.

17

Phase-Locked Loops

Everyone is familiar with phase-locked loops (PLLs) from having been one on many occasions, when dancing, playing in an orchestra, or marching to a cadence count, for example. The input to a PLL is always a periodic signal such as the beat of music, the motion of a baton, or a cadence count, for the examples just mentioned. The PLL tracks the frequency and phase of the input and can provide several types of output that will be described presently. The tracking is achieved by using feedback; hence PLLs are a type of feedback loop with the usual stability problems.

Uses of PLLs

The scale on which PLLs are used is enormous. For example, every modern television set has about five PLLs. Two are used to provide horizontal and vertical synchronization of the picture, and a third locks the color subcarrier to the color burst in the composite video signal. Still another PLL is used in a frequency synthesizer, which is part of the electronic tuner, and one more is usually used to demodulate the sound signal. Every videocassette recorder has these PLLs and may have two more for controlling the speed of the capstan and the head drum. PLLs are also used extensively in other consumer electronic products such as radios, camcorders, compact disk players, scanners, and modems. Thus there are hundreds of millions, if not billions, of them in use, making PLLs one of the most important applications of feedback. In addition to the enormous usage in consumer electronic products, PLLs are used very extensively in industrial electronic applications, digital communication systems, and many other fields.

Scope of Treatment

A thorough study of PLLs can easily fill entire books (Best, 1997; Gardner, 1979) and is far beyond what we can attempt in a single chapter. Therefore, we will focus mainly on the stability problem. That problem will be addressed with Bode plots and simple design curves, just as in previous chapters when dealing with ordinary loops, rather than with complicated time domain transfer functions. Some important and difficult matters other than stability, such as initial locking, will have to be skipped completely, but help is available in the references.

The Basic PLL

A basic electronic PLL is shown in Fig. 17-1. The principal components are a phase comparator, a low-pass filter (LPF), an amplifier if needed, and a voltage-controlled oscillator (VCO). The output of the VCO is a sine or square wave of constant amplitude, with its frequency proportional to the input control voltage e_c. When the PLL is locked on the input, the output of the VCO is at the same frequency as the input and the phase is approximately 90° relative to the input. Under these conditions the output of the phase comparator is nearly zero. If any significant phase error develops, that is, a departure from a 90° difference, a positive or negative output voltage from the phase comparator is developed, and this voltage, after filtering, adjusts the frequency of the VCO so as to reduce the phase error.

In most PLL block diagrams, the amplifier is not shown. It is assumed that its gain is included in the sensitivity factor of the VCO. It is also assumed that the VCO has an internal bias voltage so that its

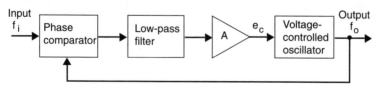

Figure 17-1 Basic phase-locked loop.

output frequency, with zero control voltage, will approximately equal the input frequency.

Types of PLLs

The basic PLL can be implemented several ways, which have been classified and named by Best (1997). When all the components are analog, the loop is called a linear PLL (LPLL). Substitution of a digital phase comparator gives the digital PLL (DPLL), while all digital components result in the all digital PLL (ADPLL). Finally, if all functions are performed in a computer by software, we have the software PLL (SPLL). We will limit our attention to the first two types, which have been used most extensively in the past. However, use of the latter two types is increasing, particularly in the areas of digital communications and process control.

Inputs and Outputs

The simplest possible input is a single sine wave. The next step up in complexity is a single periodic wave with a more complex waveform, such as a square wave or a sawtooth wave. These waves consist of a sine wave fundamental plus harmonics, which are sine waves at integral multiples of the fundamental frequency. In most cases there will also be other waves that are not frequency related to the signal of interest, and there will also be noise. The PLL must lock on a single sine wave component of the complete input and reject all other input signal components.

The basic PLL provides two outputs, the input control voltage to the VCO, and the output of the VCO, which will be a fixed amplitude sine wave or square wave. If the VCO has a highly linear voltage-to-frequency conversion constant, the control voltage to the VCO will be proportional to the frequency of the signal that the PLL is locked on. Thus the loop can function as a demodulator for frequency modulated signals such as radio broadcasts in the FM band and television sound signals. If the input signal is phase modulated rather than frequency modulated, it can be demodulated by passing the control voltage through an integrator, since frequency is the time derivative of phase.

Figure 17-2 shows how an amplitude modulated signal can be demodulated by a PLL and a few more components. The 90° phase shift gives a sine wave of fixed amplitude in phase with the component of the input that the PLL is locked on. This sine wave can be used

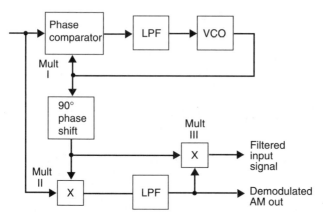

Figure 17-2 Amplitude demodulation with a PLL.

to synchronously detect the locked input, by multiplying the reference wave and the input with multiplier II and low-pass filtering the output. This AM demodulation function was the intended application of the very first PLL, invented by the French engineer de Bellecize in 1932. This method of demodulation provides much better signal-to-noise ratio than does peak rectification, which has been used far more widely. However, although an interesting combination of several analog signal processing functions, this approach is too complicated to be very economically competitive now that modern digital filtering methods are readily available. An exception to this restriction still exists at frequencies too high for digital signal processing.

If the demodulated signal is subsequently used to modulate the phase shifted output of the VCO, by multiplying the two in multiplier III, the output is a highly filtered replica of the signal that the PLL is locked on. In this mode the PLL and associated circuitry are functioning as a very narrow band filter whose center frequency automatically tracks the frequency of the input.

Preview of Main Concepts

Before starting a detailed study of the loop components and how they function, we will mention briefly a few concepts that are fundamental to understanding PLLs. Because of some rather unique aspects of PLLs, it is helpful to have all these basic concepts in mind when studying any part of the loop in detail. First, phase, not frequency, is the basic variable that is controlled by the PLL, even though frequency is also controlled. Phase is more fundamental in that when it is locked, the frequency must be locked also. By contrast, the frequency could be locked, yet with any value of phase whatsoever. Thus PLLs are named correctly. However, frequency may seem to be the primary variable when dealing with frequency modulated signals and when the VCO is referred to as a voltage-to-frequency converter, characterized by a constant for the conversion ratio.

The second fundamental concept follows from the first: In terms of phase, the VCO is an integrator; its Bode gain plot is a straight line with a slope of -6 dB/octave, and its phase plot is $-90°$ at all frequencies. This concept leads directly to the third basic point. In order to have good loop stability, the low-pass filter cannot contribute very much additional phase shift around the unity gain frequency. Consequently, its attenuation must be nearly independent of frequency in that region. Also, since additional attenuation at substantially higher frequencies is of little value, the entire filter roll-off must be well below the unity gain frequency.

A fourth point, unrelated to the first three, is that despite considerable similarity in appearance, linear PLLs are fundamentally different from the feedback loops studied previously because of multiplication, rather than subtraction, of the input signal and the feedback signal. The difference is less pronounced, however, when the phase comparison is performed digitally.

Analog Phase Comparison

An analog phase comparator, or phase detector, is always implemented with a four-quadrant analog multiplier, which processes the signals in accordance with a trigonometric identity given by Eq. (17.1).

$$(\sin x)(\sin y) = \tfrac{1}{2}\cos(x - y) - \tfrac{1}{2}\cos(x + y) \qquad (17.1)$$

For PLLs, $x = 2\pi f_i t$ and $y = 2\pi f_o t + \phi$, leading to Eq. (17.2) when the loop is locked so that $f_o = f_i$:

$$[\sin(2\pi f_i t)][\sin(2\pi f_i t + \phi)] = \tfrac{1}{2}\cos \phi - \tfrac{1}{2}\cos(4\pi f_i t) \qquad (17.2)$$

The phase of the second term has been ignored, since that term is unwanted and is essentially eliminated by the low-pass filter, making its phase irrelevant. Since the feedback is negative, the PLL will adjust the phase of the feedback signal so as to minimize the output of the phase comparator. Minimum output will occur when the phase is almost $90°$ relative to the input sine wave that the PLL is locked on, since the cosine of $90°$ is zero. However, a small phase error must exist to provide the control signal to the VCO. The greater the sensitivity of the VCO or the larger the amplification factor A in Fig. 17-1, the smaller the phase error needed.

The effect of phase angle on the product, when both inputs to the multiplier are the same frequency, is illustrated in Fig. 17-3. Short segments of the product are shown for several phase angles. The double frequency or sum component is the same for all, but the zero frequency or difference component, which shifts the average value, obviously varies as the cosine of the phase angle.

The output of a multiplier when one input consists of the sum of two sine waves of different frequencies and the other input is a sine wave at a third frequency is shown in Fig. 17-4. The average value of the output over an extended period of time is zero, due to the orthogonality of sine functions, but the instantaneous value is not zero. Since all such products are unwanted in a PLL, a low-pass filter is normally used to attenuate them.

The frequency spectrum of all the signals in Fig. 17-4 is shown in Fig. 17-5. The sum frequencies will all be higher than the VCO frequency, represented by e_3 in Fig. 17-4, making them easy to block with a filter, but the difference frequencies are lower than the VCO frequency and are usually troublesome. The phase of such frequencies is irrelevant, so the absolute value of the difference frequency can be plotted. This is equivalent to reflecting about the zero-frequency axis any frequency that comes out negative. This concept is helpful when part of the input signal consists of a continuous noise spectrum. Multiplication shifts this spectrum up and down by the VCO frequency, and any part that is shifted below zero is reflected to positive values. Noise from parts of the original noise spectrum that overlap after shifting and reflecting add as the square root of the sum of the squares, provided that noise in different parts of the spectrum is uncorrelated.

The concept of frequency shifting is also helpful for understanding the effect of input wave forms on the multiplier output. If one input to the multiplier is a sine wave and the other is a square wave, the lowest additional difference frequency component in the output will result from the third harmonic of the square wave. It will be at twice the fundamental frequency, the same as the sum component resulting from the fundamental, and hence will not cause any extra trouble. Thus two sine waves, one sine wave and one square wave, or two square waves, as we will see in the next section, result in no unwanted output components lower than twice the fundamental frequency. However, if the VCO output is a square wave, any components of the input signal, including noise, that are close to the harmonics of the VCO output will

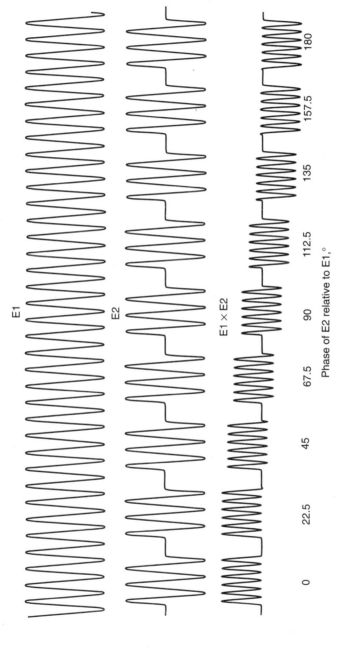

Figure 17-3 Product of two sine waves of the same frequency, showing dependence on phase angle.

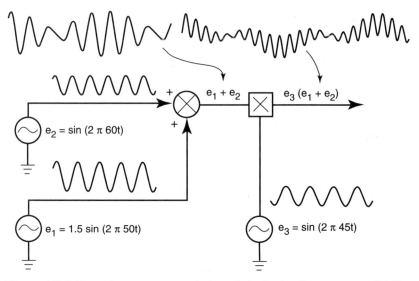

Figure 17-4 Time domain representation of products of sine waves of different frequencies.

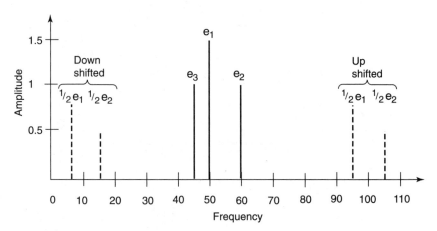

Figure 17-5 Frequency domain representation of products of sine waves of different frequencies.

cause low-frequency difference components that may be difficult to filter out. If the input has such components, a sine wave output from the VCO is desirable and an analog phase comparator is necessary.

The amplitude of each component of the multiplier output is one-half the product of the amplitudes of the two input signals. Hence the gain through the multiplier, and thus the loop gain, is directly proportional to the amplitude of the input signal. Loop gain has such a pronounced effect on loop stability that some means of controlling the amplitude of the input, such as automatic gain control, or clipping, may be necessary.

Digital Phase Comparison

If both inputs to the phase comparator are symmetrical square waves of constant amplitude, an analog multiplier would still function satisfactorily as a phase comparator. However, under these conditions, a digital logic circuit is almost always used instead. Compared to an analog multiplier, a digital logic circuit will usually be cheaper, faster, insensitive to small variations in the amplitudes of the input signals, and can also have other advantages.

The most popular type of digital logic phase comparator is called a phase-frequency detector (PFD), which consists of two D-type flip-flops and a few other components, suitably interconnected (Best, 1997, p. 93). The greatest advantage of the PFD is that when the loop is not locked, the PFD functions as a frequency comparator and generates an output that pulls the VCO toward the locked condition. As soon as the loop locks, the PFD switches over automatically to being a phase comparator to keep the phase locked. In this mode the PFD functions essentially the same as a considerably simpler logic phase comparator, the "exclusive OR" (XOR) gate. Since we are concerned mainly with stability, which is a factor only when a PLL is in the locked state, and since the two types of digital phase comparators just mentioned perform essentially the same when the loop is in the locked state, we will simplify our discussion by limiting attention to the XOR phase comparator. The symbol for an XOR gate and its truth table are shown in Fig. 17-6a and b, while Fig. 17-6c shows the output when the two inputs are 90° out of phase, the normal operating condition. The output duty cycle is then 50 percent, so the average voltage, which will not be attenuated by the low-pass filter, is $V/2$, where V is the high, or "one," logic level of the XOR output and the low, or "zero," logic level is 0 V. If the XOR gate is a CMOS type, the high output level will be the same as the supply voltage.

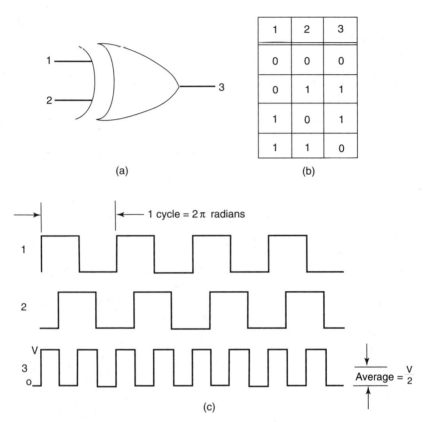

Figure 17-6 Exclusive OR gate. (a) Symbol for the gate. (b) Truth table. (c) Wave forms.

The output duty cycle and the average voltage both vary linearly with phase shift over a limited range, becoming 100 percent and V volts, respectively, if the phase shift increases to 180° and 0 percent and 0 V if the phase shift decreases to zero. Thus the sensitivity factor, or gain, of the XOR gate used as a digital phase comparator is V volts for π rad of phase shift, or V/π volts per rad. Extremely fast XOR gates are available, so the transfer function is essentially a constant gain factor, independent of frequency.

For some applications two signals that are exactly 90° out of phase with each other are useful. In a digital loop where square waves are desired, the phase relationship can be obtained very easily by interconnecting two J-K flip-flops as shown in Fig. 17-7. The input signal does not need to be symmetrical. This configuration also divides the frequency by a factor of 4. If this division is not wanted, it can be can-

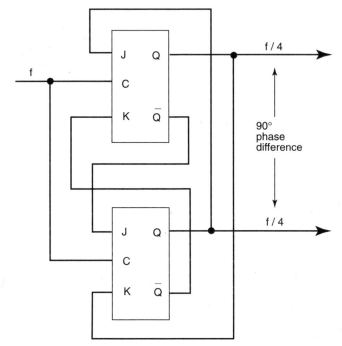

Figure 17-7 *J-K* flip-flops interconnected so as to generate symmetrical square waves that are exactly 90° out of phase.

celed several ways, one of which will be illustrated in connection with frequency synthesis.

Voltage-Controlled Oscillators

Since a low-pass filter is the next component encountered after the phase detector when going around the loop in a forward direction, it might seem logical to discuss the filter characteristic at this point. However, it turns out to be better to skip over the filter to the VCO because the VCO characteristics must be understood in order to understand what is needed and acceptable in the way of filter characteristics.

Voltage-controlled oscillators, or voltage-to-frequency converters as they are sometimes called, are usually characterized on data sheets by a single parameter, the conversion sensitivity in hertz per volt, which we will call K_1. It is an incremental factor, or slope, since the VCO will usually have a nonzero output frequency with zero input voltage. However, since phase is the output of interest and the VCO integrates, the proper conversion constant has the units of radians per volt-second. More useful is the unity gain frequency of the VCO, since that plus the fact that the VCO is an integrator gives the complete Bode gain plot if there are no other time constants. A reasonable guess for the unity gain frequency is simply the frequency per volt input K_1, and we will now show that this is correct. The unity gain frequency of an op amp integrator was found easily in Chap. 4 using the frequency domain transfer function. A similar approach for a VCO is feasible, but could be confusing because it involves two frequencies—the frequency of the input voltage variation and the output frequency of the VCO. Accordingly, it is simpler to work in the time domain this time, and we start by reviewing the op amp integrator of Fig. 4-3. An input of 1 volt-second results in a charge q on the capacitor of $1/R$ coulomb, which develops a voltage of q/C volts across the capacitor, or $1/T$ volts, where $T = RC$. This voltage is also the output voltage, and it is also equal to $2\pi f_c$, since $T = 1/(2\pi f_c)$ for an integrator.

For a VCO, an input of 1 volt-second causes an output phase change of K_1 cycles, or $2\pi K_1$ rads. As with the op amp integrator, this value is equal to $2\pi f_c$ so that $f_c = K_1$, and the integrator time constant is $1/(2\pi K_1)$. The value of f_c allows the VCO Bode gain plot to be drawn immediately.

Extra Time Constants in a VCO

In a typical electronic VCO, the only significant time constant is often the integrator time constant. Data sheets for commercial voltage-to-frequency converters rarely mention any time constants at all, although the integrator time constant can be calculated from the conversion factor. However, there may be some time constants that are not obvious, while in other situations there can be some that are quite evident. We will now look at a digital PLL used to provide precise control of speed of rotation. This application of a PLL illustrates the presence of extra time constants in a VCO, besides being of interest in its own right. PLLs are often used to control the speed of the tape drive capstan in helical-scan videocassette recorders. An identical digital PLL is used to control the speed of the head drum. The block diagram is shown in Fig. 17-8. The manufacturer refers to this system as a digital servo loop, which it certainly is, but it is also a digital PLL. From the latter viewpoint, the components to the right of the vertical broken

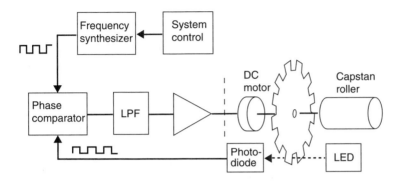

Figure 17-8 A digital servo loop.

line constitute a VCO. Since the output is phase, which is a function of the position of the notched disk in the tachometer, while the input voltage controls the angular velocity of the motor, it is obvious that this VCO is functioning as an integrator. The Bode plot will have a slope of −6 dB/octave because of the time constant as an integrator. In addition, for this VCO, there will be a mechanical time constant due to the combined inertia of the motor armature, capstan, and tachometer, as well as an electrical time constant due to the inductance of the armature winding. Consequently, the complete Bode gain plot will have the same shape as the Bode plot for a dc motor having a voltage input and position output, as shown in the lower curve of Fig. 7-1. This sameness of shape is logical since, with the tachometer shown, phase is a measure of position. Purely electronic VCOs will have the same shape Bode plot, but the increases in slope will usually occur at much higher frequencies, and the time constants responsible for them are often much less obvious.

The input frequency is provided by a frequency synthesizer in the control section of the recorder. Quite a few values are needed to give the desired speed for normal, slow motion, freeze frame, cue, jet cue, review, and jet review, all for standard play, long play, and extended play operation. For the recorder under discussion, the input frequency for the capstan servo is zero for freeze frame, 80 Hz for slow motion in extended play, 719.4 Hz for normal play or record in standard play mode, and about 6 kHz for the fastest jet cue. Another synthesizer provides the input frequency for the drum servo. It is always nearly 600 Hz, but is varied slightly for each condition to provide proper picture synchronization.

An optical digital tachometer is shown in Fig. 17-8. The output is a square wave of constant amplitude, independent of velocity. If an electromagnetic digital tachometer is used, the output amplitude, as well as the frequency, would be a function of velocity and the signal would have to be amplified and clipped to provide the proper logic level for the digital phase comparator.

Returning to the VCO, this example illustrates how there can be at least three time constants. Most electronic VCOs have only one time constant specified, indirectly, but there are always more, albeit obscure. Sometimes they are short enough to be negligible; sometimes not. If time constants have been ignored and loop stability seems worse than expected, take a close look.

The Low-Pass Filter

We are now in a position to take up the low-pass filter characteristic. The filter in a PLL is a compromise between three rather incompatible requirements. First, it should attenuate heavily all sum and difference frequency signals from the phase comparator, other than the zero frequency difference signal resulting from the input component that the PLL is locked on. Second, it should pass the so-called zero-frequency component with minimal attenuation. Since this component actually has considerable bandwidth, the second requirement conflicts with the first. The bandwidth needed when the PLL is demodulating a stereo multiplexed FM broadcast signal, for example, is more than 30 kHz. The third requirement is a filter characteristic, which, in combination with the characteristics of the other loop components, will not degrade loop stability excessively.

The third requirement actually simplifies matters considerably by virtually ruling out all the esoteric modern filters that would ordinarily be used to resolve the conflict between the first two requirements to best advantage. That is because a sharp demarcation between the pass band and the stop band cannot be achieved without more phase shift than is compatible with good loop stability. The result is that most PLLs use a very simple filter, namely, a phase retard network, also called a lag-lead network in some servo and PLL literature. When its gain characteristic is combined with the integrator characteristic of the VCO, the solid curve in Fig. 17-9 results. If there are any more time constants in the VCO or in other loop components, the extra time constants will cause additional roll-off as indicated by the dashed line. This type of open-loop characteristic was discussed in Chap. 11. It was recommended there that the extent of the -12 dB/octave segment be restricted so that the maximum phase does not exceed about 135°, pro-

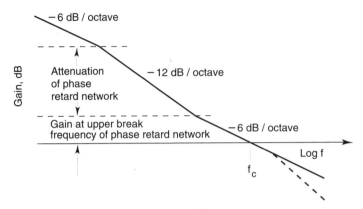

Figure 17-9 Bode gain plot for typical PLL.

viding a comfortable 45° cushion against the risk of conditional stability. This cushion should not be confused with the loop phase margin, which is a totally different parameter, relating to the phase at the unity gain frequency only.

The conflicting requirements encountered with PLLs frequently necessitate accepting a smaller value for the cushion and occasionally accepting conditional stability. The curve in Fig. 17-10 shows just what the phase shift and cushion will be as a function of the filter attenuation for a single phase retard network and for two cascaded buffered phase retard networks spaced out enough to give a flat maximum phase. The maximum phases for the two filters do not look a lot different, but a factor of about 2, which is worthwhile, appears in the cushion. Bode plots for a combination of two phase retard networks providing a total of 40 dB attenuation with a flat maximum phase shift of 70°, or a 20° cushion in a PLL, are shown in Fig. 17-11.

If the cushion is reduced substantially below 45°, extra care should be exercised to ensure that it will not vanish completely under abnormal conditions. When the cushion is reduced to zero or less, giving conditional stability, special precautions must be taken to prevent momentary reductions in loop gain or complete instability may result.

A phase retard characteristic for the loop filter is usually selected mainly because of the third requirement, but the characteristic is not highly effective for either of the first two requirements already mentioned. Consequently, several alternatives have been explored, and utilized to a very limited degree. One idea is to omit the filter completely, since it is not doing a great deal of good. With this option there is no peaking and overshoot caused by a filter, and the desired signal is

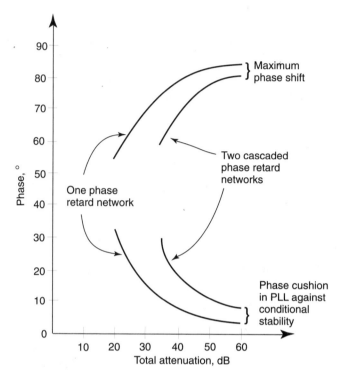

Figure 17-10 Maximum phase shift as a function of total attenuation for phase retard networks and resulting phase cushion.

passed freely. However, with most inputs, undesired sum and difference frequency components from the phase detector, not being attenuated at all, will cause excessive phase jitter in the VCO. This option is usually viable only when the input consists of a single signal component with a good signal-to-noise ratio. An alternative in the opposite direction is to use a filter with a slope steeper than the slope of a phase retard network. The slope will still have to be positioned well below the unity gain frequency. The steeper slope will reduce phase jitter, but at the expense of loop stability, and will usually result in conditional stability. Another alternative is a slope of −6 dB/octave all the way from zero frequency up to the ending frequency somewhat below the unity gain frequency. A filter with this characteristic is called a PI filter, for proportional plus integral. However, as we noted in Chap. 14, only a certain amount of low-frequency gain is useful, and more can result in unnecessarily high recovery time after various abnormal conditions. Also, in a PLL the PI characteristic forces the loop to be on the verge of

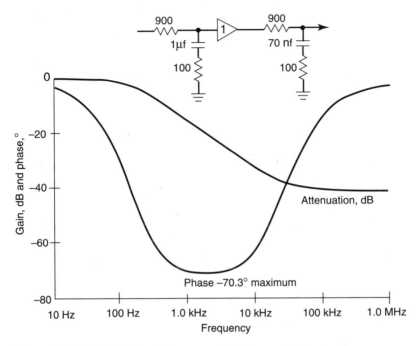

Figure 17-11 Bode plots for two cascaded phase retard networks.

conditional stability, which is almost always undesirable. All things considered, the best compromise for most PLLs is either a simple phase retard network or two separated phase retard networks.

The amplifier shown in Fig. 17-1 is normally an op amp with local feedback to give a fixed gain that is flat with frequency to a value far above the loop unity gain frequency. Instead of using an op amp this way, it could be incorporated into an active filter having positive gain where desired. However, when the loop characteristic of Fig. 17-9 is wanted, the combination of a phase retard network and an amplifier will provide it as well as any active filter.

Closed-Loop Characteristics

Except when there is a frequency divider in the feedback path, which will be considered later, the output phase is essentially identical to the input phase when the loop is locked, aside from a 90° offset. Thus the closed-loop gain, in terms of phase, is unity, or 0 dB. The loop is similar in many ways to the unity gain voltage follower discussed in Chap. 2 and could be called a phase follower. The closed-loop gain is 0 dB from zero frequency up to the unity gain frequency. Above that frequency the closed-loop gain is the same as the forward gain, as discussed in Chap. 8. The forward gain is also the open-loop gain in this case, since the feedback factor is unity. The possibility of peaking somewhat below the unity gain frequency is discussed in the next section.

The bandwidth of the closed-loop characteristic is equal to the open-loop unity gain frequency. The bandwidth can be increased by increasing the amplifier gain until the effect of additional time constants, indicated by the broken line in Fig. 17-9, starts to degrade loop stability excessively.

The rise time of the response to a step change of input phase is most easily calculated from the closed-loop time constant determined from the unity gain frequency. The time constant value is simply $1/(2\pi f_c)$, where f_c is the open-loop unity gain crossover frequency. For very stable loops, the rise time will be about 2 time constants, decreasing to about 1 time constant for less stable loops. The decrease in rise time as stability decreases is more pronounced than for second-order loops with monotonically increasing slope, as shown in Fig. 12-5. The shape of the response is also significantly different (see Fig. 17-14), and is discussed further on.

Loop Stability

The solid curve in Fig. 17-9 is a special case of open-loop gain characteristic, but it is very common for PLLs. With this curve, loop stability depends on just two parameters, the gains at the two slope transitions. It is worth carrying out the analysis for a variety of value sets and plotting the results for subsequent use. This is a good place to resort to SPICE simulations again, and the resulting curves for step function overshoot and peaking are shown in Fig. 17-12. The curves are applicable to any feedback loop, of course, but the characteristic of Fig. 17-9 is encountered most often for PLLs.

Both peaking and overshoot increase very little for attenuations greater than 40 dB. Thus a PI filter with infinite attenuation, because of infinite gain at zero frequency, has almost the same effect on peaking and overshoot as a phase retard network with 40 dB attenuation.

The curves in Fig. 17-12 have some very interesting features. In general, the curves are similar to those presented earlier in Figs. 10-3 and 12-3, except for being reversed from right to left. The reversal results from the need to shift the characteristic used for Fig. 17-12 in the opposite direction vertically (compared to the characteristic used for Figs. 10-3 and 12-3) in order to move the unity gain crossing into a region of

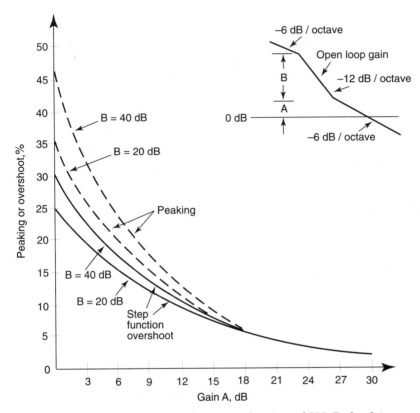

Figure 17-12 Peaking and overshoot as a function of PLL Bode plot parameters.

lower slope. However, there are also striking differences between the curves of Fig. 17-12 and the earlier curves. For the earlier curves, a displacement of 12 dB, or a factor of 4, between the break point and the unity gain crossing was sufficient to eliminate overshoot and peaking for a second-order system. For the characteristic shown in Fig. 17-9, however, even 30 dB is not sufficient to eliminate either. Thus, it is virtually impossible to avoid some peaking and overshoot in a PLL, except for the rare instances where the low-pass filter can be omitted. Even with the very gentle filtering of a phase retard network, overshoot and peaking of at least a few percent are almost inevitable. For fairly small values of gain at the slope transition, the peaking and overshoot are so high for the characteristic of Fig. 17-9 that the curves were not extended to negative values of gain. Another interesting feature of the curves in Fig. 17-12 is that the difference between peaking and overshoot is much less than for the earlier curves, becoming negligible for low values.

The most interesting feature of all, and one that is of considerable general importance, is the fact that for this characteristic, damping factor and phase margin are not related to peaking and step function overshoot in the same manner as they are for the second-order characteristic considered in Chap. 9. This is particularly evident if we look at the situation where the asymptotic slope transition coincides with the unity gain crossing for both types of characteristics under consideration. Fig. 17-13 depicts the situations graphically, with the solid curve representing the open-loop gain characteristic of a typical PLL. It is similar to the characteristic for which the curves of Fig. 17-12 were developed. The broken-line curve represents a characteristic typical of most ordinary loops after appropriate compensation, with an open loop slope that increases monotonically with frequency. For both the characteristics shown in Fig. 17-13, the damping factor is 0.5 and the phase margin, 45°. However, the closed-loop peaking and overshoot, as determined with SPICE simulations or other means, are much greater for the solid characteristic. Therefore, it must be concluded that neither damping factor nor phase margin by itself determines peaking and overshoot. The curves found in many feedback control texts relating overshoot to damping factor are almost always for characteristics with a shape similar to that of the broken-line characteristic of Fig. 17-13, although that restriction is rarely stated. Such curves do not give correct results for charcteristics with the shape of the solid-line characteristic in Fig, 17-13, or for characteristics of various other shapes. Fortunately, curves presented in books on PLLs usually relate to char-

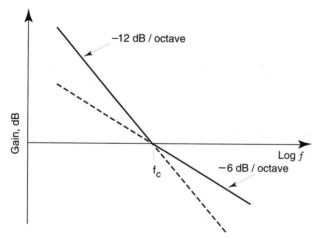

Figure 17-13 Characteristics with identical damping factor but different peaking.

acteristics with the shape of the solid-line characteristic shown in Fig. 17-13.

Stability with an Additional Time Constant

Figure 17-14 shows a similar open-loop characteristic except with an additional short time constant causing the slope to increase to -12 dB/octave again above the unity gain frequency. With this characteristic it is desirable to have the unity gain frequency in the middle of the -6 dB/octave segment, on a log frequency scale, since the phase will be least there. This condition is imposed by making $f_3/f_c = f_c/f_2$. SPICE simulations then give the values of peaking and overshoot; they are plotted against the ratio f_c/f_2 in Fig. 17-14. For these simulations the attenuation of the phase retard network was 80 dB, making the results almost identical to what would be obtained with a PI filter or with any value of attenuation greater than about 40 dB. For attenuation of 20 or

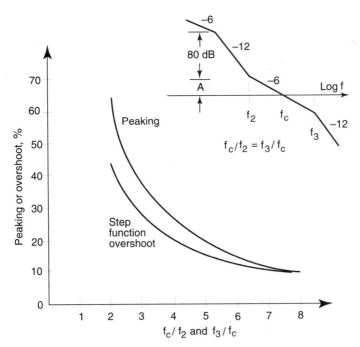

Figure 17-14 Peaking and overshoot with extra time constant in loop.

30 dB in the phase retard network, the peaking and overshoot would be somewhat less, as was evident in Fig. 17-12. The peaking and over-shoot are also somewhat less if two separated phase retard networks are used, resulting in slightly less maximum slope and phase.

The curves relate to phase, so if frequency is the parameter of main interest, the results must be interpreted appropriately, based on the fact that frequency is the time derivative of phase.

The Order of PLLs

An integrator characteristic alone, provided in a PLL by the VCO, results in a first-order type 1 loop, as discussed near the beginning of Chap. 8. When a phase retard network is added as a filter, the combination is usually referred to as a second-order system. Even when this nomenclature is not used explicitly, it is often implied by calculating the damping factor, which is defined only for second-order systems. However, if the attenuation of the phase retard network is minuscule, performance will still be essentially that of a first-order loop, and it is not reasonable to call the loop a second-order system. Thus, questions are raised about how much attenuation is needed to justify a change in designation, and whether such a change is ever warranted.

As the attenuation of the phase retard network is increased from a very small value, the shape of the first part of the step function response does not change from that of a first-order system. Even for large values of attenuation, or an infinite value for the solid curve of Fig. 17-13, the slope of the step-function response increases from zero to its maximum value at the time of the step, just as for a first-order system. This increase is evident in Fig. 17-15, which shows the closed-loop step-function responses of the two open-loop characteristics of Fig. 17-13. The immediate jump of the output slope to its maximum value at the time of the input step accounts in part for the considerably faster rise of the solid characteristic.

However, as the attenuation of the phase retard network is increased, features of second-order loop response appear. These include peaking and step function overshoot, which are nonexistent for first-order loops of the type discussed in Chap. 8. So what is a PLL, in the absence of any other time constants, a first- or a second-order system?

The order of the characteristics studied in Chaps. 8 and 9 was the highest power of ω in the denominator of the open-loop transfer function, with ω not appearing in the numerator at all. The transfer func-

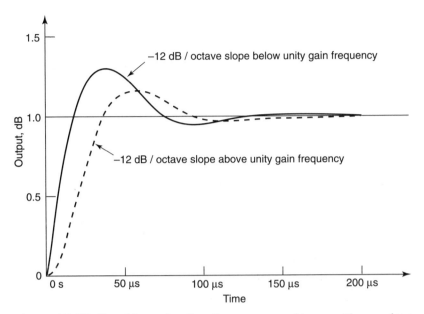

Figure 17-15 Closed-loop step function response of loops with open-loop characteristics show in Fig. 17-13.

tion of a loop with an integrator and a phase retard network with attenuation factor k is given by Eq. (17.3).

$$w(j\omega) = \frac{1 + j\omega T_1}{1 + j\omega k T_1} \times \frac{1}{j\omega T_2} \qquad (17.3)$$

All nonfrequency dependent gain factors in the loop, such as amplifier and phase comparator gain, have been consolidated into the integrator time constant T_2. Here ω appears in the denominator to the second power, but also in the numerator to the first power. At very high frequencies, where ωT_1 is much greater than 1, or if k is nearly 1, the system is essentially a first-order system. However, at low frequencies with a substantial value of k, the transfer function has some of the characteristics of a second-order system. A damping factor can be calculated from the quadratic function of ω that constitutes the denominator of the transfer function, exactly as for any second-order system. However, it will not have the same significance as a damping factor calculated for a transfer function in which ω does not appear in the numerator.

The phase margin is defined and calculated exactly the same for both characteristics shown in Fig. 17-13. For both, the phase at the unity gain frequency will be 90° from the integrator, plus 45° from the other component, regardless of whether the attenuation begins or ends at the unity gain frequency. Thus the total is 135° for each characteristic, leaving a 45° phase margin.

After this more mathematical perspective, the answer to the question about the order of a PLL is still somewhat ambiguous, and may be just a matter of semantics. The important thing is to be aware that the shape of the Bode plot affects the significance of damping factor and phase margin. When the more direct approach of using Bode plots and design curves is followed, as in this book, it is necessary to use curves determined specifically for the shape of the Bode plot under consideration.

Frequency Synthesis

A frequency synthesizer generates an output at a prescribed frequency ratio relative to an input signal, usually from a high-precision crystal oscillator. There are two main approaches. Direct synthesis involves various methods of generating new frequencies without recourse to PLLs. This method has the virtue of good spectral purity, since the phase jitter of PLLs is not encountered. Direct synthesis also results in very short settling time when the output frequency is switched. This feature is particularly important in frequency-hopping applications in communications and radar systems. Indirect synthesis, which uses one or more PLLs, is more economical and hence is widely used despite some limitations. We will confine our discussion to this type of frequency synthesis and to the rudimentary synthesizer shown in Fig. 17-16. The output of the counters may be asymmetrical for some or all values of M or N. Therefore, flip-flops are used to further divide the output frequency of each counter by two, resulting in perfectly symmetrical square waves for inputs to the digital phase comparator. The overall frequency multiplication ratio is N/M, where N and M are integers. The counters are digitally programmed to divide by values that will result in the desired output frequency. The counters and the phase comparator are digital, but the filter and VCO are analog.

Commercial frequency synthesizers are considerably more complicated than the simple system shown in Fig. 17-16 and must deal with a host of difficult problems. Chapter 10 of Gardner's *Phaselock Techniques* (1979) gives a good introduction, with references to more thorough treatments. We will only look at two matters that are related to the stability problem. First, when a counter is inserted in the feedback path,

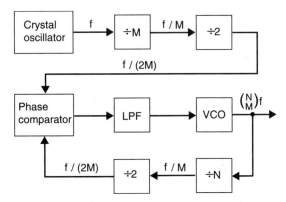

Figure 17-16 Rudimentary frequency synthesizer.

without any other change in the loop, the loop gain is reduced by the factor by which the counter is dividing the frequency. An easy way to see this is to note that the phase error needed to provide the control voltage to the VCO must increase by the division factor in order to cause the higher output frequency, just as if the value of amplifier gain had been decreased by the same factor instead of inserting the frequency divider. For most feedback loops, reducing the loop gain results in better stability. Thus it may come as a surprise, at first, when adding the counter results in impaired loop stability. The explanation is obvious when the open-loop gain plot of Fig. 17-9 is recalled. With this characteristic, lowering the loop gain moves the unity gain crossover point to a region of steeper slope and hence greater phase shift. The impairment of stability will be greatest when the division factor moves the unity gain frequency to the middle of the -12 dB/octave segment on a log frequency scale. This situation is clearly one in which omission of the loop filter would be advantageous if it could be tolerated. Unfortunately, omission of the filter aggravates phase jitter, which is particularly objectional in a frequency synthesizer. An alternative is to increase the value of amplifier gain A after the counter is added to the feedback path so as to restore the original open-loop characteristic.

This discussion raises the question of why a steady-state phase error is needed to provide the drive signal to the VCO, considering that the loop includes integration. PLLs are good at generating brainteasers like this, and we will leave this one for the reader to think about. Another subject in the same vein is the discussion, absent in this chapter and in most texts on PLLs, about the polarity of the gain A needed to make the feedback negative. Hint: look at the phase comparator output for large values of phase difference.

The other aspect of stability of special importance to frequency synthesizers is phase jitter. All kinds of digital noise, ground noise, and other disturbances will impact a PLL in a frequency synthesizer. The amount of phase jitter resulting from noise excitation will increase markedly as the stability of the loop decreases. Thus good stability is essential for reasonable spectral purity in the output of frequency synthesizer using PLLs.

A Numerical Example

Since PLLs are significantly more confusing than ordinary feedback loops, a numerical example can be helpful. Suppose we have a VCO with a conversion factor of 10 kHz/V, and the VCO has an additional time constant of 1 μs. A phase retard network with 40-dB attenuation will be used as the loop filter, and a CMOS exclusive OR gate, with logic levels of 0 and 5 V, will provide digital phase comparison. The complete PLL, with some of the values determined, appears in Fig. 17-17. We want to find the amplifier gain A and filter parameters that will result in about 20 percent overshoot to a phase step function input. We also want to find what the closed-loop bandwidth will be with those values.

From Fig. 17-14 we find that for 20 percent overshoot the unity gain frequency must be about 3.5 times lower than the break frequency

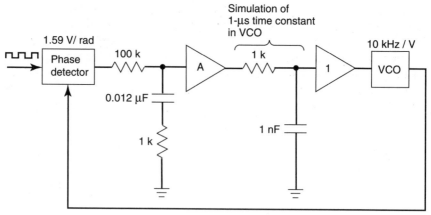

Figure 17-17 PLL used for numerical example.

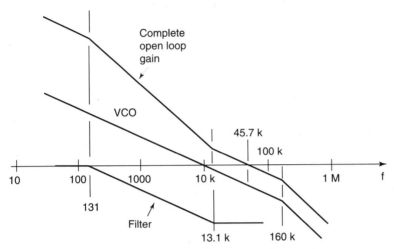

Figure 17-18 Bode plot of PLL used for numerical example.

caused by the extra time constant in the VCO. The break frequency caused by the 1 μs time constant is $f = 1/(2\pi x\ 10^{-6})$, or about 160 kHz. Therefore, the open-loop unity gain frequency must be 160/3.5 kHz, or 45.7 kHz. This is also approximately the PLL bandwidth, since the feedback factor is unity. The break frequencies for the filter then need to be 45.7/3.5 kHz = 13.1 kHz and 13,100/100 = 131 Hz, as shown in Fig. 17-18.

Finally, we need to determine the value of A needed to provide the desired stability. A gain factor of 4.57 × 100 = 457 V/rad through the phase comparator and amplifier is needed to shift the 10 kHz unity gain frequency of the VCO up to 45.7 kHz and to make up for the attenuation factor of the filter, which is 100. The gain factor through the phase comparator alone is $5/\pi = 1.59$ V/rad. Therefore, an amplifier gain of 457/1.59 = 287 is needed.

This example is another illustration of how the apparent speed of a device, the VCO in this case, can be increased by overdriving it momentarily when a sudden change in output is necessary. The example also shows that when the overdrive is developed by feedback, which is usually necessary to achieve the proper drive values as a function of time, the amount of speedup possible is limited by short time constants, which impair loop stability excessively if the forward gain needed to provide overdrive is made too high. Independent of this limitation, the amount of improvement achievable by overdriving a device is also limited by nonlinearities. In most feedback loops, however, the limitation imposed by time constants will come into play well before limitations imposed by nonlinearities.

Other Computer Simulations

The subtleties of PLLs make computer simulations particularly attractive. We have just used SPICE to study the small signal linear response of PLLs. When the nonlinearities involved in locking, holding lock, and other features of PLL operation are involved, simulation with SPICE is much more difficult. A better alternative is to use a custom PLL simulation program. Several are available from manufacturers of PLL integrated circuits, and one is included with Best's *Phase-Locked Loops* (1997).

18
Comparison of Methods

To be outstanding in any field, one must not only be able to use the tools of the trade expertly but also be able to pick the optimum tool for every job. This skill requires, of course, thorough knowledge of the capabilities and limitations of all the available tools. In the area of feedback control, the range of tools is so broad that it is not practical or desirable to try to cover them all in one book, with the consequence that a completely self-contained comparison is impossible. Nevertheless, some perspective on why the Bode-plot approach is considered to be particularly advantageous is important, and we will undertake that here.

Before getting into details, a few general considerations warrant comment up front. The method that is best for one individual may not necessarily be best for the next, since different people have different aptitudes and biases. Also, all methods have some merit and can complement one another nicely. Bode himself allowed that the complex frequency concept, although not necessary, is of value in facilitating mathematical analysis (Bode, 1945, p. 29). Finally, we should remember that engineers have never been particularly noted for being open-minded. Having said all this, we will now proceed with an attempt to show that Bode plots are the method of choice for most loops at the simple to intermediate level of complexity.

Comparison of different methods is facilitated by a classification. While this can be done in various ways, all more or less arbitrary, the breakdown shown in Fig. 18-1 is appropriate for our purposes. This classification excludes methods for dealing with nonlinear systems,

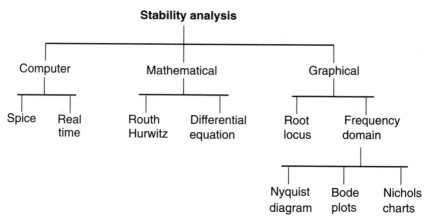

Figure 18-1. Classification of various methods of feedback control.

sampled data systems, adaptive systems, and a few of the more esoteric methods, which are for the most part beyond the scope of this
book, as well as being unnecessary for most systems.

Computer-Based Methods

Computer-based methods have become very important since the use
of microprocessors and personal computers has become routine. Two
general approaches are shown in the classification. In one, indicated
by SPICE, the system components such as op amps, transducers, and
compensation networks are entered into the program, and it calculates
the response for any desired test input. Compensation is carried out
largely by adjustment of component values through trial and error,
guided by concepts such as those developed in this book. Thanks to
the rapid and effortless calculation of outputs after each parameter
change, the process is fully practical.

In the other numerical method shown, the computer or microproces-
sor functions as part of the loop in real time, performing operations
such as comparison, amplification, and compensation digitally. The
reference input and feedback signals are converted to digital signals
by analog-to-digital converters, and the output is usually converted
back to analog by a digital-to-analog converter. A number of commercial programs develop the detailed program that the computer uses in
real time, based on performance requirements and component specifications provided by the user.

Both approaches are very powerful because of the enormous power
of modern microprocessors, and the latter has the merit that, theoreti-

cally at least, an individual with very little background in mathematics or engineering can develop a successful system. Both approaches have the disadvantage of being overkill for many requirements, with consequent loss of convenience, such as being able to function in the field without having a computer present. In addition, they obscure intuitive sense of what is going on, which is still of some importance and which helps one exploit the power of computers to full advantage.

Mathematical Methods

Turning to the mathematical methods, the differential equation method was the first ever used, but it is too cumbersome for everyday use. When the equations are converted to a simpler form by subjecting them to Fourier or Laplace transformation, the method becomes more practical; we used a type of frequency domain analysis in part for our treatment of first- and second-order systems. Even for them, however, considerable reliance on graphical methods, particularly for designing the loop compensation, will usually reduce the total effort required.

The Routh-Hurwitz criterion is mainly of historical interest, as it relates only to complete instability, rather than to degrees of stability, and provides little direct guidance for loop compensation.

Graphical Methods

Graphical methods are generally easier, and hence have been widely used, and are also the subject of more controversy as to the best method. The root locus technique, a graphical procedure in the complex frequency plane, has been strongly promoted and is perhaps the most widely used. The main virtue of this method, ostensibly, is that it provides time domain results more easily and directly than frequency domain methods. Attention is focused on the location of closed-loop poles (roots of the system characteristic equation) and zeroes in the complex frequency plane and on the path, or locus, traversed by each pole as the loop gain is increased from zero to a high value. When the loci have been constructed, additional effort is needed to extract performance parameters such as rise time and overshoot.

The drawbacks can be inferred from a review of a number of texts by root locus gurus, averaged to protect individual identities. Bad-mouthing of frequency domain techniques begins in the second paragraph of the preface and continues intermittently but unabated for 500 pages as Laplace transform theory, root locus methods, and related material are developed. The mere fact that 500 pages are needed speaks to the simplicity, or lack thereof, of the approach. Then on page 501 a transport lag is encountered for the first time, although with no explicit recognition or discussion of the important concepts of minimum phase and excess phase. On page 502 it is admitted, correctly, that transport lags pose a serious problem for the root locus method, and Nyquist diagrams or Bode plots are suggested as alternatives. By page 503 Nyquist diagrams have been jettisoned also, leaving the reader with Bode plots alone, about which he or she has learned little or nothing while struggling through the first 500 pages. Lest this situation be mildly disconcerting, the reader is reassured on page 504 that with Bode plots the addition of a transport lag is only a minor complication. As we saw in Chap 16, it is a little worse than that, although not excessively so. The somewhat overly optimistic assessment results from failure to appreciate how simple the Bode plot approach can be in the absence of excess phase.

Even without a transport lag, the root locus technique is not all that simple. A thorough grounding in Laplace transform theory is needed to understand it, and a set of 10 rules (more or less, depending on which text you are reading) for the construction of the root loci must be memorized. In addition, an ingenious special tool, the Spirule©, is needed to speed up the great number of calculations required, and another set of rules for its use must be kept in memory also. Unfortunately, the aspiring young engineer who can't find the overshoot without both rule sets and a gadget is apt to be categorized with the proverbial individual who couldn't find part of his or her own anatomy with both hands and a spotlight.

This brings us to the three principal frequency domain techniques. Nyquist diagrams are polar plots of open-loop gain and phase, with frequency a parameter along the curve. Stability depends on where the curve passes in the neighborhood of the point representing unity gain and 180° phase shift. As with the Routh-Hurwitz criterion, the condition for complete instability, that is, oscillation, is obvious enough, but the relationship between the curve position and percent overshoot of a fairly stable system, for example, is not so clear. In principle, contours of constant gain margin or phase margin could be shown on the graph, allowing those parameters to be determined graphically, and performance characteristics could be estimated from them. However, graph paper with such contours is extremely rare, and the approach is rather indirect. Also, since gain and frequency are not logarithmic, scaling is apt to be a problem. More fundamentally, for minimum phase loops, use of both gain and phase is, from the point of view of this book, a serious defect, since they are not independent. Finally, the Nyquist plot does not give a detailed picture of the compensation needed.

Nichols charts, combining some of the features of Nyquist diagrams and Bode plots on special graph paper, provide another interesting frequency domain technique. As with Nyquist plots, both gain and phase are involved, so the objection just mentioned for Nyquist diagrams is valid when dealing with minimum phase loops. In addition, Nichols charts require special graph paper, which may not always be at hand, do not virtually draw you a picture of the compensation needed the way Bode plots do, and do not cascade components as easily. When significant excess phase is present, Nichols charts are up there with Bode plots as the only useful graphical techniques, but are still not as simple and convenient, for the reasons just cited.

Advantages of Bode Plot Methods

Finally, we want to review and summarize the reasons why we feel the Bode plot technique is the optimum method for most simple and intermediate complexity loops. The virtues of the plots themselves were summarized in Chap. 4. The method as a whole has several advantages. For minimum phase systems, concern for phase is eliminated completely, resulting in greater simplicity and clarity, with less complicated mathematics, than any other form of analysis. In particular, knowledge of the complex frequency plane and Laplace transforms is rendered unnecessary. For second- and third-order minimum phase systems, the important closed-loop performance characteristics, both frequency and time domain, can be ascertained from the Bode gain plot or from system parameters with extreme ease, with the aid of a few simple curves or rules of thumb presented in Chaps. 9 and 12. It is not necessary, as alleged by many root locus enthusiasts, to perform inverse Fourier transforms to find time domain characteristics. Another great advantage is that the Bode plots virtually design the compensation for you, as shown in Chap. 11.

The other main reason for using Bode plots is that when the first major complication, a transport lag, is encountered, the method, suitably extended, is still the simplest and easiest. Its relative advantage, compared to the root locus method, is even greater with a transport lag, although all methods become more difficult. The relative advantage compared to Nichols charts may be reduced somewhat but is still substantial. It makes little sense to develop expertise with a method that will have to be abandoned at the appearance of the first major complication.

References

Best, R. E., *Phase-Locked Loops,* 3d ed., McGraw-Hill, New York, 1997.

Bode, H. W., *Network Analysis and Feedback Amplifier Design,* D. Van Nostrand, Princeton, N.J., 1945.

Del Toro, V., *Electromechanical Devices for Energy Conversion and Control Systems,* Prentice Hall, Englewood Cliffs, N.J., 1968.

Gardner, F. M., *Phaselock Techniques,* 2d ed., John Wiley & Sons, New York, 1979.

Graeme, J. G., "Bode Plots Enhance Feedback Analysis of Operational Amplifiers," *EDN,* pp. 163–172, February 2, 1989.

Graeme, J. G., Tobey, G. E., and Huelsman, L. P., *Operational Amplifiers,* McGraw-Hill, New York, 1971.

Lee, Y. W., "Application of Statistical Methods to Communications Problems," *MIT Research Laboratory of Electronics Technical Report,* no. 181, September 1, 1950.

Thomason, J. G., *Linear Feedback Analysis,* McGraw-Hill, New York, 1955.

Valley, G. E. Jr. and Wallman, H., "Vacuum Tube Amplifiers," *MIT Radiation Laboratory Series,* vol. 18, McGraw-Hill, New York, 1948.

Weaver, H. J., *Application of Discrete and Continuous Fourier Analysis,* John Wiley & Sons, New York, 1983.

Index

ABOUT THE AUTHOR

Walter S. Friauf (Bethesda, MD) has over 30 years' experi-
ence in electronic circuit design. He has served as Chief of
the Electrical and Electronic Engineering Section of the
Biomedical Engineering and Instrumentation Program at the
National Institutes of Health and was previously a Senior
Engineer at Texas Instruments. Mr. Friauf holds a BSEE
(Massachusetts Institute of Technology) and MEE (University
of Virginia).